Design and Development of Fighting Vehicles

6 00 209611 9
TELEPEN

Design and Development of Fighting Vehicles

R. M. Ogorkiewicz
M.Sc.(Eng.), A.C.G.I., D.I.C., A.M.I.Mech.E.

MACDONALD : LONDON

SBN 356 01461 4

Published by
Macdonald & Co (Publishers) Limited
Gulf House, 2 Portman Street London W1
Made and Printed in Great Britain by
Hazell Watson & Viney Ltd.
Aylesbury, Bucks

To the memory of
my father
Colonel M. A. Ogorkiewicz

Preface

THE purpose of this book is to provide an up-to-date account of the design and development of armoured fighting vehicles—an account called for both by their military importance and the general interest which they arouse.

The account presented here does not, of course, claim to cover every aspect of the design and development of fighting vehicles. It is, in fact, mainly concerned with the principal facets of the development of battle tanks, tracked armoured personnel carriers and wheeled armoured vehicles since the end of the Second World War in 1945, and with the current state of their design.

The background of earlier developments is only presented in outline, since many books have already dealt with the history of armoured fighting vehicles. They include my earlier book, *Armour—The Development of Mechanised Forces and Their Equipment*, which was published in 1960 in Britain and the United States, and subsequently in Italy. The reception given to this book provided much of the encouragement for the preparation of the present volume while many of the ideas contained in it stem from a number of articles which I have written during the past six years for *The Engineer*, *Armor*, *The Royal United Service Institution Journal*, *Brassey's Annual* and the *New Scientist*.

R.M.O.

London, 1967.

Contents

List of Figures in Text
with Acknowledgements

List of Plates
with Acknowledgements

11. French 2C heavy tank with a turret-mounted 75 mm gun.

12. French type B battle tank designed in the mid-twenties.

13. British Light Infantry Tank which attained 30 m.p.h. during trials in 1922.

14. Vickers Medium Mark I.
Vickers-Armstrongs Ltd.

15. British Independent heavy tank with five turrets.
Vickers-Armstrongs Ltd.

16. British Medium Mark III tank with three turrets.
Imperial War Museum

17. Carden Loyd Mark VI tankette with head covers.
Vickers-Armstrongs Ltd.

18. Polish TKS tankettes developed from the Carden Loyd Mark VI.

19. Light Tank Mark I built by Vickers-Armstrongs in 1930.

20. Russian T-38 amphibious light tanks.
Imperial War Museum

21. Vickers-Armstrongs 6-ton tank, single turret model.
Vickers-Armstrongs Ltd.

22. Russian T-26C developed from the Vickers-Armstrongs 6-ton tank.
Imperial War Museum.

23. Landsverk 10, or Strv m/31, light-medium tank of 1930.
A. B. Landsverk

24. Ceskomoravska Kolben Danek tank assembled in Switzerland as the Pz.39.
Swiss Army

25. United States T3 medium tank built by J. W. Christie in 1931.

26. Russian Christie-type BT-7 tank.
Imperial War Museum

27. French H-35 light infantry tank.
Imperial War Museum

28. British Infantry Tank Mark I.
Ministry of Defence, Crown Copyright Reserved

29. Pz.Kpfw. II with a 20 mm gun, the most numerous German tank during the 1940 campaign in France.
Imperial War Museum

30. German Pz.Kpfw. IV 75 mm gun tank of 1939–41.
Imperial War Museum

31. Russian T-34 medium tank.

32. Russian KV-1 heavy tank.
Imperial War Museum

33. German Panther medium tank with a 75 mm L/70 gun.

34. German Tiger II heavy tank with an 88 mm L/71 gun (side plates partly removed to reveal internal layout).

35. British Churchill II infantry tank with a 40 mm 2-pounder gun.
Imperial War Museum

36. British Cromwell I cruiser tank with a 57 mm 6-pounder gun.
Birmingham Railway Carriage & Wagon Co. Ltd.

37. Pilot model of the U.S. M3 medium tank with a hull-mounted 75 mm gun.
U.S. Army

38. United States M4A1 medium tank with a 75 mm gun.
U.S. Army

39. United States M4A3 medium tank with a 76 mm gun.
U.S. Army

40. United States M26 heavy tank with a 90 mm gun.

41. British Centurion 1 with a 76·2 mm 17-pounder gun.
Ministry of Defence, Crown Copyright Reserved

42. Centurion 7 with an 83·4 mm 20-pounder gun.
Ministry of Defence, Crown Copyright Reserved

43. Centurion 9 with a 105 mm gun.
Ministry of Defence, Crown Copyright Reserved

44. Conqueror 120 mm heavy gun tank.
Ministry of Defence, Crown Copyright Reserved

45. Russian T-34/85 medium tank.

46. Russian T-54 medium tank with a 100 mm gun.

47. Russian-designed T-54 tank delivered by China to Pakistan in 1966.
The Associated Press Ltd.

48. Russian T-62 battle tanks with 115 mm guns.
The Associated Press Ltd.

49. Prototype of the AMX 50 battle tank with a 100 mm gun.
French Army

50. French AMX 50 battle tank with a 120 mm gun.
French Army

51. United States M46 medium tank.

52. United States M103 120 mm gun heavy tank.
U.S. Army

53. Four tanks built in the United States during the fifties: left to right, M103 120 mm gun tank, M48 and M47 90 mm gun tanks and M41 76 mm gun light tank.

54. United States M48A2 90 mm gun tanks.
U.S. Army

55. United States T95 medium tank.
U.S. Army

56. United States M60 105 mm gun battle tank.
U.S. Army

57. Japanese Type 61 medium tank.
Japan Ordnance Association

58. Swiss Pz.58 tank with a 90 mm gun.
Swiss Army

59. Swiss Pz.61 tank with a 105 mm gun.
Swiss Army

60. Prototype of the French AMX 30 battle tank.
French Army

61. Production version of the AMX 30 battle tank.
French Army

62. Prototype of the German Leopard battle tank.
German Army

63. Production version of the Leopard battle tank.
German Army

64. Vickers 37-ton battle tank built for the Indian Army.
Vickers Ltd.

65. British Chieftain battle tank with a 120 mm gun.
Ministry of Defence, Crown Copyright Reserved

66. Pre-production version of the Swedish S-tank.
A. B. Bofors

67. S-tank, or Strv 103.
Swedish Army

68. Swiss G-13 version of the German-designed and Czech-produced Jagdpanzer 38t of the mid-forties.
Swiss Army

69. Jagdpanzer (Kanone) built for the German Army during the early sixties.
Rheinmetall GmbH

70. United States M60A1E1 battle tank with a 152 mm gun/missile launcher.
U.S. Army

71. United States M551 Sheridan air-transportable reconnaissance vehicle with a 152 mm gun/launcher.
U.S. Army

72. British Tetrarch, the first tank to go into action by air, being loaded into a Hamilcar glider.
Imperial War Museum

73. United States T9E1 prototype of the M22, the first tank designed and built for airborne operations.
R. J. Icks

74. French AMX 13 light tank.
French Army

75. AMX 13 light tank being unloaded from a Breguet Deux Ponts aircraft.
S.A. des Ateliers d'Aviation Louis Breguet

76. T41 prototype of the U.S. M41 light tank.
U.S. Army

77. United States T92 light tank.
Aircraft Armaments Inc.

78. Russian PT-76 amphibious reconnaissance tank.

79. United States M551 Sheridan being dropped by parachute from a transport aircraft.
Allison Division of General Motors

80. Chieftain tank armed with a high-velocity 120 mm gun.

81. M50 Ontos armed with six 106 mm recoilless guns.
U.S. Marine Corps

82. SS-11 guided missile fired from a Hotchkiss light carrier.
Nord Aviation

83. AMX 13 tank with SS-11 missiles.
French Army

84. Malkara missile fired from a FV.1620 Hornet.
Ministry of Defence, Crown Copyright Reserved

85. Swingfire, a second generation anti-tank guided missile.
British Aircraft Corporation Ltd.

86. Shillelagh guided missile.
Aeronutronic Division, Ford Motor Company

87. Shillelagh missile fired from a M551 Sheridan.
Aeronutronic Division, Ford Motor Company

88. Prototype of the AMX 13 tank with a F.L.10 trunion-mounted, or oscillating, turret.
French Army

89. AMX 13 with a F.L.12 oscillating turret mounting a 105 mm gun.
French Army.

90. United States T92 tank with a cleft turret.
Aircraft Armaments Inc.

91. United States M60A1E1 tank with a 152 mm gun/launcher mounted in a turret with reduced frontal area.
Aeronutronic Division, Ford Motor Company

92. Prototype of the U.S. M60A1 battle tank with an elongated turret surmounted by a machine-gun cupola.
U.S. Army

93. S-tank compared with a conventional, turreted, Centurion tank.
A. B. Bofors

94. United States M41 tank with welded turret and hull.

95. United States T48 tank with a one-piece cast turret and hull.

96. United States T196 (later M109) 155 mm self-propelled howitzer with a turret and hull welded out of aluminium alloy armour.
U.S. Army

97. United States T235 175 mm self-propelled gun with nylon blanket protection.
U.S. Army

98. Russian T-34 tank with a Christie type suspension.

99. Horstmann-type bogie suspension and steel-tyred, resilient road wheels of the Conqueror heavy gun tank.

100. Epoxy resin bonded glass fibre road wheel light enough to be lifted by a young boy; in the background a M41 tank with single-pin track.
The Firestone Tire & Rubber Co.

101. United States M48 tank with a double-pin, double-block track.
Chrysler Corporation

102. End connectors of a double-pin single-block track.

103. United States M56 air-portable 90 mm self-propelled anti-tank gun with a band track.
U.S. Army

104. LVTP5 amphibians negotiating surf.
U.S. Marine Corps

105. LVTH6 amphibian of the U.S. Marine Corps followed by LVTP5 carriers.
U.S. Marine Corps

106 Covers over the outlets from the water jet propulsion unit of the Russian BTR-50P armoured personnel carrier.

107. Outlets of the water jet propulsion unit of the Russian PT-76 tank shown open and the right outlet discharging water.

108. Vickers 37-ton battle tank swimming with the aid of a collapsible flotation screen.
Vickers Ltd.

109. Centurion tank with rigid panel flotation equipment.
Ministry of Defence, Crown Copyright Reserved

110. German Leopard fording submerged to the turret top.
German Army

111. United States M60A1 tank emerging after the first underwater crossing of the Rhine in 1963.
U.S. Army

112. German Sd.Kfz.251/10 half-track armoured personnel carrier.

113. United States M3 half-track carrier.
U.S. Army

114. United States M44 Armoured Utility Vehicle, the forerunner of several contemporary armoured personnel carriers.
R. J. Icks

115. United States M75 Armoured Infantry Vehicle.
Ordnance Division, F.M.C. Corporation

116. United States M59 Armoured Infantry Vehicle with a ·5 in. machine-gun cupola.
Ordnance Division, F.M.C. Corporation

117. LVTP6 amphibian developed for the U.S. Marine Corps from the basis of the M59 carrier.
Ordnance Division, F.M.C. Corporation

118. United States M113 Armoured Personnel Carrier.
Ordnance Division, F.M.C. Corporation

119. M113 carrier propelling itself in water by means of its tracks.
Ordnance Division, F.M.C. Corporation

120. Demonstration of the ease of exit from the M113 carrier due to its rear ramp.
Ordnance Division, F.M.C. Corporation

121. M113 carrier fitted with machine gun shields.
Ordnance Division, F.M.C. Corporation

122. M113 carrier modified into the XM734 with firing ports for fighting from within the carrier.
Ordnance Division, F.M.C. Corporation

123. British FV.401 Cambridge carrier.
Ministry of Defence, Crown Copyright Reserved

124. Prototype of the British FV.432 armoured personnel carrier.
Central Office of Information, Crown Copyright Reserved

125. FV.432 armoured personnel carrier with the flotation screen erected and the trim vane hinged forward.

126. French AMX-VTT carrier with a 7·5 mm machine-gun turret.
French Army

127. Rear view of the AMX-VTT showing the crew facing outwards.
French Army

128. Prototype of the HS.30 carrier with the A.26 Hispano Suiza 20 mm gun turret.
Hispano Suiza (Suisse) S.A.

129. Production version of the German HS.30 carrier.
German Army

130. Austrian Saurer 4K3F carriers.
Austrian Army

131. Side view of the Saurer 4K3F carrier.
Oesterreichische Saurerwerke A.G.

132. Saurer Tartaruga carrier built to a Swiss Army requirement.
A. G. Adolph Saurer

133. Mowag Pirate armoured carrier.
Mowag Motorwagenfabrik A.G.

134. Japanese SU Type 60 carrier.
Japan Ordnance Association

135. Henschel HW-K 11 carrier built for Mexico.
Rheinstahl Henschel A.G.

136. Swedish Pbv 301 armoured personnel carrier.
Swedish Army

137. Swedish Pbv 302 armoured personnel carrier.
Swedish Army

138. Pbv 302 carrier swimming offshore.
Swedish Army

138a. Ghosted view of the Swedish Pbv 302 carrier with the V-shaped trim vane hinged forward
Swedish Army

139. United States XM 701 Mechanised Infantry Combat Vehicle.
Pacific Car & Foundry Co.

140. Russian BTR-50P armoured personnel carrier.

141. Daimler-Benz MTW-1 on trials in 1929.
R. J. Icks

142. German Sd.Kfz.234/2 Puma armoured car.
Imperial War Museum

143. Daimler II Armoured Car.
Daimler Co. Ltd.

144. Ferret Mark 2 scout car.
Ministry of Defence, Crown Copyright Reserved

145. Ferret Mark 2/6 with Vigilant guided missiles.
Ministry of Defence, Crown Copyright Reserved

146. Ferret Mark 5 with mock-up turret for Swingfire missiles.
British Aircraft Corporation Ltd.

147. Chevrolet-built M38 armoured car.
U.S. Army

148. Prototype of the Alvis Saladin armoured car.
Ministry of Defence, Crown Copyright Reserved

149. Production version of the Alvis Saladin.
Alvis Ltd.

150. Alvis Saladin with the flotation screen erected.
Alvis Ltd.

151. Alvis Saracen armoured personnel carrier.
Ministry of Defence, Crown Copyright Reserved

152. FV.1611 armoured truck.
Ministry of Defence, Crown Copyright Reserved

153. Gendron-Somua armoured car.

154. Panhard E.B.R. with F.L.11 turret.
French Army

155. Panhard E.B.R. with F.L.10 turret.
French Army

156. Panhard E.B.R. with a 90 mm gun in a F.L.11 turret.
French Army

157. Panhard A.M.L. with H.E.60 turret.
French Army

158. Panhard A.M.L. with a 90 mm gun in a H.90 turret.
French Army

159. Panhard A.M.L. with Entac missiles on a S.A.M.O.1160 launcher.
French Army

160. F.N. 4RM/62F armoured car with a 90 mm gun.
Fabrique Nationale d'Armes de Guerre S.A.

161. Russian BTR-152 carrier with a central tyre pressure control system.

162. Russian BRDM amphibious reconnaissance car with guided missiles.

163. A rear-engined development of the BRDM reconnaissance car.

164. Russian BTR-60P amphibious armoured personnel carrier.

165. Cadillac Gage Commando.
Cadillac Gage Co.

166. Cadillac Gage Commando propelling itself across a lake by means of its wheels.
Cadillac Gage Co.

167. Chrysler MAC-1 armoured car built for Mexico.
Chrysler Corporation

168. Chrysler Special Warfare Armoured Transporter.
Chrysler Corporation

169. D.A.F. YP-408 armoured personnel carrier.
Van Doorne's Automobielfabriek N.V.

170. Mowag MR 8-01 carrier with four wheel steering.
Mowag Motorwagenfabrik A.G.

171. Mowag amphibious armoured personnel carrier.
Mowag Motorwagenfabrik A.G.

172. Mowag amphibious carrier propelling itself across a lake by means of screws.
Mowag Motorwagenfabrik A.G.

173. Mowag Roland with special bullet proof tyres.
Mowag Motorwagenfabrik A.G.

174. Shorland patrol car.
Short Brothers & Harland Ltd.

CHAPTER 1

The Evolution of Fighting Vehicles

ARMOURED fighting vehicles stem from ideas which evolved over a very long period of time. Some of the ideas may, in fact, be traced as far back as the second millennium B.C., when horse-drawn war-chariots were widely used in the Near East for fighting with missile weapons—as mobile weapon platforms, which is the basic function of tanks today.

Other ideas, focused on the protection of armoured fighting vehicles, can be traced back through the wheeled siege towers and battering rams used during the Middle Ages to similar devices used by the Assyrians as early as the ninth century B.C. A more recent form of the same idea of a protected vehicle may be found in the battle cars proposed in 1335, in France, by Guido da Vigevano, by Leonardo da Vinci in 1484, and by others, down to J. Cowan, who took out a patent in Britain in 1855 for a turtle-shaped wheeled armoured vehicle based on the contemporary steam tractor.

However, it was only at the turn of this century that armoured vehicles began to take practical form. By then the essential mechanical elements had been developed and, in particular, the traction engine and the motor car had become available for application to military purposes. In consequence, the former was used for the construction of an armoured vehicle and the latter was converted into a gun carrier.

Thus, the first armoured vehicle was an armoured road locomotive with a train of armour-plated wagons. It was built by John Fowler and Company, of Leeds, for use in the South African War of 1899–1902, and was obviously inspired by the earlier use of armoured railway trains. The first armed vehicle was a de Dion-Bouton powered quadricycle on which F. R. Simms mounted a Maxim machine gun and exhibited in Richmond, Surrey, in June 1899 (Pls. 1 and 2).

The sequel, inevitably, was the construction of a vehicle which was both armed and armoured. Such a vehicle, with an open-top boat-shaped armoured hull, appeared in April 1902, at the Crystal Palace, in

London (Pl. 3). Its construction was promoted by F. R. Simms but it was built to an order of Vickers, Sons and Maxim Ltd., and its layout followed the drawings produced six years earlier by E. J. Pennington.

Similar ideas were evident elsewhere. In the latter part of 1899 a machine-gun-armed motor car was built in the United States by Major R. P. Davidson and in 1902 a partially armoured machine-gun car was exhibited at the Paris Salon de l'Automobile by the Société Charron, Girardot et Voigt, which then proceeded to develop a fully armoured car with a turret. The latter was completed in 1906, by which time a turreted, fully armoured car had also been built in Austria, by the Austro-Daimler Company.

To complete the evolution of the essential features of armoured fighting vehicles it only remained to adopt tracks as an alternative to wheels. This final step became inevitable when tracked tractors began to appear but there was no incentive for it to be taken until after the outbreak of the First World War in 1914. Until then further development of armoured cars languished and proposals for tracked vehicles failed to arouse interest on the part of the conservative-minded military authorities.

For example, this was the case with a proposal for an armoured self-propelled tracked field gun made in 1903 by Captain Levavasseur of the French Artillery and a similar proposal made five years later by Major Donohue of the British Army Service Corps. Similarly, the design of a tracked armoured vehicle evolved in 1911 by an Austrian officer, G. Burstyn, was rejected, in turn, by the Austro-Hungarian and German general staffs, and the War Office showed no interest in another design, submitted to it in 1912 by an Australian engineer, L. E. de Mole.

The outbreak of the First World War brought about a radical change in the situation. Its opening stages of mobile warfare accelerated the development of armoured cars and the subsequent onset of trench warfare brought forth new proposals for tracked armoured vehicles. Most of the proposals sprung from the idea of making armoured cars capable of moving off the roads and the first tracked armoured vehicle was, in fact, improvised in Britain, in July 1915, by mounting the body of a Delaunay-Belleville armoured car on the chassis of an American Killen-Strait tractor (Pl. 5). The origins of this experimental improvisation lay with the Royal Naval Air Service, which in 1914 created an Armoured Car Division to support the operation of its aircraft in France and whose officers began to look beyond their road-bound armoured cars, based on Rolls-Royce and other passenger car chassis, to cross-country vehicles capable of attacking enemy trenches. Their ideas were backed by the

First Lord of the Admiralty, Winston S. Churchill, who, in February 1915, set up a Landships Committee to develop them. The result was a series of experiments and designs which led to the construction of Little Willie, the first tracked armoured fighting vehicle, or tank, designed and built as such (Pl. 6).

Little Willie first ran in September 1915, but was quickly superseded by a second model (Pl. 7). This had a long, overhead track layout, with guns mounted in sponsons, which gave it a peculiar rhomboidal silhouette and which was devised to improve its trench-crossing capability. The requirement that it should cross wide trenches came from Lt. Col. E. D. Swinton, who already had some ideas of his own on tracked armoured vehicles, and was conveyed to the Admiralty by the War Office, which had by then taken an interest in tanks. When completed, the second model was demonstrated to the Army chiefs and immediately afterwards, in February 1916, the War Office placed an order for 100 tanks of the same type.

Almost simultaneously and quite independently of the events in Britain, tanks were also developed in France, due largely to the initiative of General J. E. Estienne. Like Little Willie, the original French Schneider design amounted to an armoured box on a tractor chassis and the first production order, for 400, was also placed in February 1916 (Pl. 8). But French tanks did not go into battle until April 1917, whereas British tanks were first sent into action on September 15, 1916.

At the time only 49 could be made available and the very first action of the British tanks on the Somme met with relatively little success. But a year later, on November 20, 1917, at Cambrai, 474 tanks were concentrated on a narrow front and in a surprise assault over suitable ground achieved a spectacular break-through, which was repeated in August 1918, at Amiens, where 604 tanks were used.

The battle of Cambrai vindicated the original tactical concept of tanks as vehicles for assaulting enemy trenches but left unresolved the second of the two contemporary problems, namely that of following up a successful assault. Tanks had clearly proved capable of breaking through the strongest trench lines but, in their original form, they were unable to exploit a break-through. They could crush thick belts of barbed wire, cross wide ditches and knock out enemy strong points while they themselves were immune to machine gun fire. But they were slow and their endurance was limited to the short range assault for which they were designed. In fact, the original, 27 to 29-ton Mark I to Mark V tanks had maximum speeds of about 4 m.p.h. and a theoretical range of 20 to 40 miles while in practice their speed and range were even lower.

In consequence, there grew a demand for a lighter, faster type of tank which could penetrate into the enemy rear areas after the heavier tanks had broken through. In answer to this came the Medium A, which had a maximum speed of 8 m.p.h. and a range of 80 miles. It met with some success in 1918 and it was followed by the design of other medium tanks but before they could be tried the war came to an end.

When the First World War ended in 1918, Britain had produced 2,636 tanks but few of these remained in operational order and fewer still were of use beyond the siege-like conditions of trench warfare under which they were introduced. France, on the other hand, was left with a relatively high proportion of the 3,870 tanks it had produced and almost all of its tanks were of the light Renault F.T. type, which was more adaptable (Pl. 9). Together with those completed after the war, there were, in fact, 3,737 Renault F.T. in 1921. This meant that the French Army had more tanks than all the other armies put together which, together with its prestige, made it dominate the post-war scene where its doctrine was followed by others.

The doctrine of the French Army was that tanks should be subordinate to the infantry, which satisfied tradition and suited the tanks it had. This confined tanks to the limited role of an auxiliary and tended to concentrate attention on infantry-accompanying tanks, of which the Renault F.T. was the prime example. Tanks of this type were slow and lightly armed and though the Renault F.T. proved effective at Soissons, in July 1918, as well as smaller engagements, they represented to a progressively smaller extent what could be done. But the doctrine of a subordinate role fitted well with traditional ideas about the primacy of the infantry, which made it all the more acceptable to the military leaders.

The first to follow the example of the French Army were the United States and Italy, the only other countries, apart from Germany—which produced about 20—to embark on the manufacture of tanks during the First World War. Both assigned their tanks to infantry support and both also copied the Renault F.T., the United States in the M1917 light tank (Pl. 10), 952 of which were completed after the war, and Italy in the Fiat 3000, of which 100 were built. In both countries, as well as France and elsewhere, tanks of the Renault F.T. type remained as the principal armoured equipment well into the thirties and even when improved vehicles became available they were still confined to the same limited role of infantry support. Moreover, in some respects, little effort was made to improve on the Renault F.T. For instance, the most numerous French tank in 1939, the Renault Model 1935, or R-35, had the same short 37 mm gun as its predecessor, as it was still regarded only as an auxiliary to the infantry.

The French Army was not, however, unaware of the need for more powerful tanks, if only for leading infantry assaults. It had, in fact, taken the lead in developing powerfully armed tanks. Its original Schneider and St. Chamond tanks already had hull-mounted 75 mm guns, when the heavier British tanks were armed with 57 mm guns or even only with machine guns, and the 2C "break-through" tanks completed after the war were the first to have 75 mm guns mounted in turrets (Pl. 11). Development of 75 mm gun tanks continued during the twenties and eventually led to the 30-ton type B tank (Pl. 12). But by the time this tank was finally produced in 1936 it was overtaken by other, later developments.

In the meantime Britain had taken the lead in developing the mobility of tanks, technically and operationally. Even before the First World War ended the engineering staff of the British Tank Corps had conceived of a medium tank with a maximum speed of 20 m.p.h. and a range of 200 miles. Out of this came the Medium D, designed by Lt. Colonel P. Johnson and built in 1919. But even its performance was improved upon in 1922 by the smaller but similar Light Infantry Tank, which attained 30 m.p.h. (Pl. 13). Moreover, both tanks were amphibious, at least to a limited extent. However, they also had troublesome features and so the first British post-war production order went to Vickers Ltd., for an 11-ton tank which became known as the Vickers Medium (Pl. 14). Altogether 160 tanks of this type were delivered between 1923 and 1928, and they became virtually the only tanks the British Army had until the early thirties, as well as being the only tanks produced in quantity anywhere in the world during the mid-twenties.

The Vickers Mediums were less ambitious than Johnson's designs but they were, nevertheless, fast enough to give the British Army a considerable advantage over others, which were still thinking in terms of the 4·8 m.p.h. maximum speed of the Renault F.T. They were, in fact, capable of about 20 m.p.h. and their performance stimulated the Royal Tank Corps to develop new, more mobile tank tactics.

The Medium D had already inspired Colonel J. F. C. Fuller to propose, in 1918, a more mobile use of tank units in raids against objectives behind enemy lines. In 1922 Captain B. H. Liddell Hart made an even more remarkable proposal for the combination of tanks with infantry mounted in armoured carriers into fully mechanised divisions. Some of the new ideas were explored in a series of experiments which began with the Experimental Mechanised Force assembled in 1927 on Salisbury Plain, but their outcome were two divergent lines of development, neither of which made the most effective use of tanks.

One line of development, inspired by the idea of tanks operating by themselves, like warships, and embraced by the tank enthusiasts, led to the creation of armoured formations composed very largely of tanks. These represented an advance in mobility on the contemporary infantry, or cavalry, divisions but their unbalanced composition confined them to the limited role of exploiting successes won in battle by other formations, which horse cavalry had previously performed. The other line of development was dictated by the traditional ideas about the preeminence of the infantry which reasserted themselves in part and led to the creation of specialised tank units for cooperating with the infantry at its own slow pace.

So, paradoxically, the quest for new methods of employing tanks resulted in the creation of two categories of tanks and tank units, in keeping with the traditional division of armies into "horse" and "foot". This was foreshadowed in a 1929 British Army manual on armoured forces which divided the army into "combat troops" and "mobile troops", as if mobility and fighting were incompatible. Nevertheless, this fallacious doctrine was accepted and as late as 1945 the British Army divided its tanks between armoured divisions "designed for exploitation" and tank brigades "designed for close cooperation with infantry divisions".

Similar ideas were adopted in the early thirties in Russia. They were also adopted in France and, on a smaller scale, in the United States, where the cavalry mechanised some of its units without radically changing their role while the infantry retained its own tanks.

The division between "infantry" and "cavalry" tank units resulted in the development of several different types of tanks. In Britain the production of the Vickers Mediums was followed by the design of the A.6 Sixteen-tonner and other medium tanks, which were armed with 47 mm guns for use against other tanks but whose principal armament were considered to be machine guns. In consequence, they had more than one turret, after the fashion set by the A.1 Independent, a 32-ton experimental heavy tank designed in 1925 at Vickers under the direction of Sir George Buckham, which had no less than four auxiliary machine gun turrets in addition to its main, 47 mm gun turret (Pl. 15). On the A.6 the number of auxiliary turrets was reduced to two but what remained still made for a tank which was large and expensive in relation to its fighting power (Pl. 16). Cheaper vehicles were, therefore, sought, not so much as a substitute for the medium tanks but to make up for the small numbers in which they were expected to be built.

An extreme approach to the problem of cost was initiated by Major G. le Q. Martel, who in 1925 built a one-man armoured vehicle using commercially available components. The idea of small, inexpensive armoured vehicles was developed further by J. (later Sir John) Carden in a series of designs which led to the two-man turretless Carden-Loyd Mark VI "tankette" of 1928 and then to the two-man Vickers-Carden-Loyd light tanks (Pl. 17).

The effectiveness of the tankettes was extremely limited but they were cheap to build and of some use for training. In consequence, 305 Mark VI tankettes were produced, for the British Army and for export, and they inspired the production of similar vehicles in five different countries: the Polish TK (Pl. 18), the Russian T-27, the Czech MU4, the Italian L/3 and the French UE *chenillette*. The Vickers-Carden-Loyd light tanks were a better proposition but, although they had turrets, they were still only armed with machine guns. However, they were capable of speeds of up to 30 m.p.h. and, being simple and light, they were relatively reliable, as well as inexpensive. They were, therefore, considered suitable for reconnaissance, for co-operation with medium tanks, and for a variety of security duties. As a result, several hundred were produced for the British Army and for export all over the world, and they were also copied in several countries, directly or indirectly (Pls. 19 and 20).

The number of light tanks and tankettes grew rapidly after 1929, as several countries started to produce armoured vehicles. Russia was by far the most important producer but, on a much smaller scale, tanks also began to be produced in 1930–31 in Poland, Czechoslovakia and Japan. At about the same time production was also re-started in France and a little later, in 1933, in Italy. But as the numbers of armoured vehicles increased the value of the machine-gun-armed tankettes and light tanks diminished, since they could not even fight their like. In consequence, they began to lose their popularity to somewhat heavier models armed with guns of 37 to 47 mm, in addition to machine guns, which were capable of fighting other tanks.

The fact that light tanks had to be able to fight other tanks was already recognised in the design of the experimental German Light

Tractor, which was built in 1928 and was armed with a relatively long barrelled 37 mm gun capable of defeating the armour of contemporary tanks. But gun-armed light tanks only came to the fore with the appearance of the Vickers-Armstrongs Six-Ton Tank (Pl. 21). This tank was designed at Vickers as a private venture but its original version was still influenced by the contemporary preoccupation of the British Army with machine guns, of which it had two, in two separate turrets. However, the second version, which appeared in 1930, was much more sensibly provided with a single two-man turret mounting at 47 mm gun and a machine gun. In this form it represented not only a solution superior to the Vickers-Carden-Loyd light tanks but also, potentially, a better return on money than the multi-turret medium tanks which were then being developed in Britain. However, the British Army would not consider it and it was only others who took it up.

Among the countries which purchased the Vickers-Armstrongs Six-Ton Tank was Russia, where it was promptly produced on a very large scale as the T-26, and Poland, where it was built on a much smaller scale as the 7TP. Like its prototype, the T-26 originally had two turrets but in 1933 it was fitted with a single turret with a high velocity 45 mm gun, which was as good as the guns of the contemporary British medium tanks (Pl. 22). In consequence, the T-26 could be regarded as a "light-medium" tank. This applied even more to the Landsverk 10, or Strv m/31, built in Sweden in 1930, along lines originating in Germany and similar 37 mm gun tanks built around 1935 in Czechoslovakia: the LT-35 built by the Skoda Company and the LTH built by Ceskomoravska Kolben Danek (Pls. 23 and 24).

The most successful of the "light-medium" tanks was the BT built in large numbers in Russia. This tank owed its origin to the results of several years' work in the United States by J. W. Christie on fast tanks which could run on wheels as well as tracks—an idea explored in several different forms during the twenties. The most notable outcome of this work was an experimental vehicle built in 1928, which attained a speed of 42·5 m.p.h. on tracks and was, therefore, even faster than the Vickers Sixteen-tonner or the Vickers-Carden-Loyd light tanks. A small number of T3 and T4 tanks was built from its basis for the U.S. Army between 1931 and 1936 but although they were promising they were not adopted. In the meantime two chassis of the T3 tank type had been sold by Christie to Russia, where they served as the basis for the design of the BT whose production began towards the end of 1931 (Pls. 25 and 26).

The idea of running on wheels after the removal of tracks was gradually abandoned in the BT but it retained the basic virtues of Christie's designs, which were an independent suspension with large road wheels and a very high power to weight ratio. To these was added a high velocity 45 mm gun, which was first mounted in the BT-5 of 1933. As a result, the BT was probably the most effective tank of the mid-thirties.

Because of their effective combination of characteristics, the "light-medium" tanks tended to be regarded as "universal" tanks, capable alike of supporting the infantry and of operating in "cavalry" roles. However, in so far as it meant moving at the pace of the foot soldier in face of anti-tank guns, they were not suitable for infantry support on account of their relatively thin armour. The truth of this was demonstrated in 1937, during the Civil War in Spain where BT, as well as T-26, tanks were used on the Communist side in support of infantry formations and suffered heavily.

Methods of employing tanks which deprived them of their advantage of mobility and exposed them to the full effectiveness of anti-tank fire made little sense, of course. But in France and Britain it had, at least, been recognised that if tanks were to be tied to the pace of the infantry they had to be heavily armoured. In consequence, the armour of the French infantry-accompanying tanks was increased from a maximum of 20 mm on the Renault F.T. to 40 mm on the R-35. Similarly, the British Army created a special category of "infantry tanks" whose principal attribute was the passive one of armour protection. Thus, the Infantry Tank Mark I, which was designed in 1935, was only armed with a machine gun and had a maximum speed of only 8 m.p.h., but it had armour up to 60 mm thick (Pl. 28). For comparison, contemporary light tanks had armour 10 to 15 mm thick and only a few medium tanks had armour thicker than 20 mm.

A corollary to the development by the British Army of a specialised category of infantry tanks was the evolution of another specialised category of tanks for the "cavalry" role. This consisted of "cruiser" tanks, which were a development of the earlier medium tanks. In fact, Cruiser Tank Mark I, which was designed at Vickers-Armstrongs in 1934, had essentially the same three-turret layout as the A.6 and its development, the Medium Mark III. The auxiliary turrets did not, however, reappear on the Cruiser Mark II; nor in the Mark III, whose design in 1937 was partly inspired by the Russian BT tank and which, consequently, had a Christie-type suspension. The Mark III, like the first two cruisers, also had a 40 mm gun and this together with its other characteristics put it clearly in the "light-medium" category.

For the limited mobile role for which the cruisers were intended they and the other "light-medium" tanks were adequate by themselves. But if they were to engage in fighting of any intensity they needed to be supported and eventually replaced by more heavily armed tanks, which could not only engage other contemporary tanks but which could also deliver effective high explosive fire. This meant tanks armed with 75 mm guns.

The need for a combination of 75 mm gun tanks with the "light-mediums" was clearly recognised in the German Army by 1932. This was preceded by the design in 1926, of an experimental *Grosstraktor*, which already had a turret-mounted 75 mm gun, and was followed, in 1934, by the design of the Pz. Kpfw. IV. In its original form, the Pz. Kpfw. IV weighed 17·3 tons and was not much heavier, therefore, than the contemporary "light-medium" tanks. It also had a maximum speed of 20 m.p.h., which made it about as fast. But, having a 75 mm gun, it was much better armed. In consequence, it became the most effective tank of the late thirties (Pl. 30).

The need for combining tanks of this type with the lighter models was realised less clearly in Russia even though the T-28 and T-35 multi-turret tanks armed with 76·2 mm guns were first built there in 1932–1933. But the Russians recognised more quickly than the Germans the need for the next step, namely for the replacement of all the "light-medium" tanks by a 75 or 76·2 mm gun medium tank. Thus, in 1939, on the eve of the Second World War, while the Germans were still developing the "light-medium" Pz. Kpfw. III from a 37 mm to a 50 mm gun version, the Russians were concentrating on the design of the T-34 medium tank with a 76·2 mm gun. The design of the T-34 was derived from that of the BT but it had thicker, 45 mm armour and its combination of mobility, protection and gun-power placed it well ahead of other tanks (Pl. 31).

Still heavier tanks were also being designed in Russia to replace the T-35. The result was the 43-ton KV with armour 75 mm thick (Pl. 32). This represented a very considerable increase on the protection possessed by other tanks except for the British Infantry Tank Mark II, or Matilda designed in 1937, which had armour up to 76 mm thick. But, while the KV was armed with a 76·2 mm gun, the Matilda was armed with the same 40 mm as the cruisers.

However, even 40 mm gun tanks were scarce in Britain on the eve of the Second World War. In fact, all but 80 of the 1,148 tanks produced between 1930 and the outbreak of the war in 1939 were still only armed with machine guns. Italy was even worse off as it only had 70 M/11 tanks with 37 mm guns while the rest of its total of about 1,500 were not even light tanks but L/3-type tankettes. The United States had nothing but a few experimental tanks with 37 mm guns, and about 300 machine-gun-armed light tanks. Japan had produced almost 2,000 but again only a few were armed with modern 37 mm guns.

By comparison, France had a well-found force of 2,677 modern tanks, of which 309 were armed with 47 mm guns and 172 were the type B tanks with hull-mounted 75 mm guns. But these figures paled when compared, in turn, with the number of tanks possessed by Russia as a result of a massive production programme started in 1930–31. Even then, during the first two years of production, 1,480 tanks were built and during the following six years—from 1932 to the end of 1937—21,000. Some of the early models, including the large number of tankettes, were withdrawn by 1939 but, nevertheless, the Soviet Army disposed of a stock of about 20,000 tanks, which was more than the rest of the world had put together.

But when the war began the most formidable tanks proved to be the German. This was due, however, only to a limited extent to their own characteristics. In fact, of the 3,195 tanks which Germany possessed on September 1, 1939, only 211 were Pz. Kpfw. IV. The rest, apart from 98 Pz. Kpfw. III and some command tanks, were light tanks, which were not much better than other contemporary tanks of this type and which were produced since 1933, despite the earlier decision to concentrate on tanks of the Pz. Kpfw. III and IV type.

What made the German tanks so formidable was the way in which they were organised and employed. Instead of being divided between "infantry" and "cavalry" tank units, they were all concentrated in *panzer* divisions, which combined tanks with motorised infantry and other complementary elements brought up, as far as possible, to the tanks' level of mobility. This combination provided tanks with the support they needed to perform in more than one or two limited roles and resulted in a new type of division which had greater fire power and greater mobility than other contemporary formations, and which was equally capable of obtaining a decision in battle as of mobile exploitation after it.

The idea of creating *panzer* divisions was due largely to General H. Guderian, who had correctly foreseen that they represented the most effective way of using tanks, and the first three came into being in 1935. Four years later *panzer* divisions demonstrated their effectiveness in the Polish campaign and they did so even more clearly in France in 1940. By then their number had risen to ten, and by a break through the French front followed by rapid exploitation they settled the issue of the campaign. The ten divisions contained all the German tanks in the field—2,574 out of a stock of 3,400. This was less than the French Army's total of 3,800 but the French and British tanks proved relatively ineffective because they were used piecemeal, in their limited roles. The *panzer* divisions were even more successful in relation to the numbers of opposing tanks in 1941, when seventeen of them, with a total of 3,350 tanks, spearheaded the German invasion of Russia and defeated the very much larger armoured forces of the Soviet Army.

The successes of the *panzer* divisions during the first two years of the Second World War made most major armies organise or reorganise their tanks into similar formations, which, inevitably, became their decisive element. In consequence, the outcome of the major ground operations during the remainder of the Second World War was very largely decided by the success or failure of the opposing armoured formations. This was certainly true of the fighting in Russia and Eastern Europe from 1942 to 1945, as it was of the smaller-scale operations in North Africa and of the campaigns in Western Europe in 1944 and 1945.

All this led to a tremendous increase in the production of tanks. Its magnitude is best shown by the following table of the numbers of tanks

Tank Production during the Second World War

	Germany	*Britain*	*U.S.A.*	*Russia*	*Japan*
1939	249	969	?	?	462
1940	1,460	1,399	331	2,794	1,023
1941	3,256	4,841	4,052	6,590	1,024
1942	4,278	8,611	24,997	24,668	1,165
1943	5,966	7,476	29,497	20,000	776
1944	9,161	?	17,565	17,000	342

produced by the five leading belligerents during the period from 1939 to 1944.

The production figures re-emphasise the effectiveness of the German tanks, which were hopelessly out-numbered from 1941 onwards by the tanks produced in Britain, the United States and Russia but which, nevertheless, remained a major factor in ground operations up to the end of the war in 1945. They remained effective, however, only because they were developed further, aptly and rapidly, in response to the changing situation. The most important development resulted from the initial encounters with Russian T-34 tanks. One thousand of these medium tanks had already been produced before the German invasion of Russia and they made the German Command realise that they needed tanks much more powerful than the existing Pz. Kpfw. IV. In consequence, two new models were developed and, more immediately, the Pz. Kpfw. IV was made more effective by rearming it with longer barrelled 75 mm guns.

The new 43 and 48 calibre long guns had a muzzle velocity of 2,460 ft/sec, which was almost exactly twice the muzzle velocity of the original 24-calibre long gun and gave the new version of the Pz. Kpfw. IV a small margin of superiority over other 75 or 76 mm gun tanks when it first appeared in the summer of 1942. However, one of the two new models, the Panther, was armed with an even more powerful, 70-calibre long 75 mm with a muzzle velocity of 3,070 ft/sec, which made it greatly superior to all other medium tanks when it was first produced at the beginning of 1943. In fact, the Panther was the most successful medium tank design to appear in the latter part of the Second World War, in spite of its relatively heavy and greater than intended weight of 43 tons (Pl. 33). The second of the two new models, the 56-ton Tiger heavy tank, was also superior to all tanks in its class as a result of being armed with an 88 mm gun, which had already proved itself as an anti-tank as well as an anti-aircraft weapon. It was produced even earlier than the Panther and a few were already in action near Leningrad in September 1942, but, unlike the Panther, it was replaced in 1944 by the Tiger II. This had an even more powerful, 71 instead of 56 calibres long, 88 mm gun. It also had thicker armour, as a result of which it weighed 68 tons and earned for itself the doubtful distinction of being the heaviest tank used in action during the Second World War (Pl. 34).

However, the only tank which could compete with the Tiger II was the Russian IS, or Joseph Stalin. This was a development of the KV heavy tank, which was armed in 1943 with an 85 mm instead of the original 76 mm gun. The first IS tanks were also armed with 85 mm guns, which were comparable to the 88 mm gun of the original German Tiger, but in 1944 they were rearmed with a 122 mm gun, while the 85 mm guns were mounted in an improved version of the T-34 tank, the T-34/85. At the same time the weight of both categories of Russian tanks increased relatively little, to the credit of their designers and to the advantage of their mobility. For instance, the T-34/85 weighed 32 tons compared with the 26 tons of the original T-34 and the IS 2 or 3, for all their heavy 122 mm guns, weighed only 46 tons.

As they were armed with heavier guns, the role of the heavy tanks changed. Originally they were developed mainly for breaking through well-fortified positions. But, by the time the Tigers and IS tanks appeared, their role became chiefly that of supporting the medium tanks by destroying enemy tanks at long range. The German and Soviet Armies also developed other heavy vehicles for this purpose, such as the Jagdtiger and the ISU 122. These had no rotating turrets and their guns had, therefore, limited traverse but they were, to all intents and purposes, "turretless tanks". This type of vehicle originated with the *Sturmgeschütz* or "assault guns", which the German Army introduced in 1940 for cooperating with the infantry, having rightly concluded that what the infantry needed were not heavily armoured and lightly armed "infantry" tanks but armoured vehicles capable of giving it close fire support. In 1942, the assault guns were rearmed with long, instead of short, 75 mm guns and they were transformed into tank destroyers but, in effect, they were merely an alternative to the more conventional type of tank. Compared with the latter they lacked the advantage of all-round traverse for their guns but this was often more than offset by their lower silhouette combined with the ability to carry heavier guns than the corresponding turreted vehicle and lower manufacturing costs—which is the principal reason why they figured so prominently in the German production programmes.

For all their advantages, no "turretless tanks" were built in Britain or the United States, except for a few experimental models. The British Army clung to the discredited doctrine of the two separate, narrowly specialised categories of "infantry" and "cruiser" tanks in neither of which was gun-power considered a primary requirement. Thus, the cruiser tanks were fast but their armament did not keep pace with that of other medium tanks; the infantry tanks were well armoured but they were never better armed than the contemporary cruisers and they were, consequently, grossly undergunned by comparison with Russian and German heavy tanks.

Failings in the field of armament became serious in 1942. By then British tanks had advanced beyond their earlier 40 mm guns, but not far enough. For instance, when the Crusader III cruiser tank was armed with a 57 mm gun, the Germans already had the Pz. Kpfw. IV with a long 75 mm. Similarly, when the Churchill infantry tanks re-armed with 57 mm guns arrived in Tunisia they were met by the Tiger with its 88 mm gun. It was recognised, eventually, that guns rather than machine guns were the principal tank weapons and general-purpose medium-velocity 75 mm guns were mounted in both categories of tanks but by then they were no longer adequate against enemy tanks. It was then argued, in all seriousness, that "the tank is designed with the primary object of destroying enemy unarmoured troops" and, *ipso facto*, that it should not be expected to fight enemy tanks—as if this could be avoided on the battlefield. The fallacy of such arguments was also recognised after a time but in the meantime British tanks continued to lag behind. For instance, when the Cromwell cruiser was first used in the field in 1944, its 75 mm gun armament was two years behind that of the German Pz. Kpfw. IV and almost three behind that of the Russian T-34 (Pl. 36). Even when the first few Centurions, the last of the cruisers, appeared just before the end of the war in 1945, their 76 mm 17-pounders were not basically different from the armament of the German Panther introduced two years earlier.

In the meantime, in 1943, British armoured formations had to be equipped to a large extent with American-built M4 Sherman medium tanks. These represented a somewhat belated response of the U.S. Army to the original German Pz. Kpfw. IV and as such they were relatively successful, which was all the more of an achievement considering the state of tank development in the United States at the beginning of the Second World War. In August 1940, when the requirement for a 75 mm gun tank was first established the sole basis for its development was the M2A1 medium tank, a tank whose only redeeming feature was the mechanical soundness of its components inherited from the earlier M2 light tank. The result was the M3 medium, with a 75 mm gun mounted in the right front of the superstructure and still only with a 37 mm gun in its small turret (Pl. 37). This tank was subsequently widely criticised but it could be produced more quickly than one with a turret-mounted 75 mm gun and it proved effective when used by British tank units in Cyrenaica in 1942. In any case, the prototype of a second medium tank, mechanically similar to the M2 and M3 but with a turret-mounted 75 mm gun, was built by September 1941 and began to be produced in July 1942, as the Medium Tank M4 (Pl. 38). Eventually 49,234 tanks of this type were built and they became the principal equipment of the United States, as well as British and the re-created French armoured formations. By 1944, however, the M4 was no longer adequately armed and although an improved version with a longer barrelled 76 mm gun was brought out it should by then have been succeeded by a new model (Pl. 39).

The development of a new U.S. medium tank had, in fact, started in 1942 but several factors conspired to keep the M4 in production and service. One was an obsession with numbers, created in part by the usual overestimates of enemy strength. Another was the contemporary attitude of the U.S. Army Ground Forces, which had also fallen for the fallacious doctrine that the proper role of armoured divisions was the limited one of exploitation and did not press for a more powerful tank. In consequence, it was only in the spring of 1945, that a few tanks of a more powerful type were used. This was the M26, or Pershing, heavy tank, a 41-ton vehicle with a 90 mm gun comparable to the 88 mm gun of the original German Tiger (Pl. 40).

Thus, when the Second World War came to an end the U.S. Army, as well as the British, were still behind the German in the gun-power of their tanks. But the doctrines which were largely responsible for this had become discredited and the fact that all tanks must be well armed, to be able to fight other tanks, was generally recognised. What was still not fully recognised were the advantages of concentrating tanks in fully mechanised formations, instead of dispersing them among the less mobile infantry divisions. In consequence, although the British Army abandoned the development of the narrowly specialised "infantry" tanks, it continued to divide its tanks between armoured and infantry formations. So did the U.S. Army and after the war most of its medium tanks were to be found not in the armoured but in the infantry divisions.

After the war tank development also suffered from one of the periodic waves of exaggeration of the effects of anti-tank weapons and of consequent doubts about the value of tanks, which was still wrongly supposed to lie in their armour protection. The Soviet Army did, however, maintain large armoured forces and the threat they posed as the Cold War became more intense together with the havoc wrought by Russian-built T-34/85 tanks in the opening stages of the war in Korea in 1950, gave a new impetus to the development of tanks as the most effective counter to other tanks.

Since the mid-fifties further stimuli have been provided by the development of tactical nuclear weapons, which put a premium on mobility and dispersion. This favoured the armoured forces, which were capable of effective dispersed operation in mobile battle groups. Moreover, armoured units were able to operate in relative proximity to nuclear explosions, by virtue of the protection provided by their vehicles against blast and radioactivity, first demonstrated in 1955, during American nuclear tests in Nevada. In consequence, the importance of armoured vehicles increased and particular attention has been given to armoured personnel carriers, which were originally devised to enable the infantry to keep up with tanks but which are now seen to be essential for the infantry itself.

The large-scale development of armoured personnel carriers has led to a progressive mechanisation of the infantry and this, in turn, has made possible a much more effective integration of it with tanks. In consequence, tanks have come to operate increasingly within a framework of fully mechanised tactical groupings based on mutually complementary weapons, which range from the portable weapons of the infantry, through tank guns, to the self-propelled guns or rocket lauchers of the artillery. Tactical groupings of this kind form mobile, multiple weapon systems and they represent the most effective instrument of ground defence, as well as aggression, on the pattern introduced by the *panzer* divisions.

In this setting, tanks are very clearly mobile weapon platforms. More specifically, they are a means of making heavy, direct-fire weapons more mobile, and therefore more effective, and this, ultimately, accounts for their continued importance.

CHAPTER 2

Tanks since 1945

THE most significant feature of the development of tanks since the end of the Second World War in 1945, has been the attention given to their armament. This followed from the general acceptance of the fact that their effectiveness depends, above all else, on their gun-power and provides a contrast with the days when the designers of the "infantry" tanks were preoccupied with armour protection and when the "cavalry" tanks were characterised by undergunned mobility.

The earlier, tradition-bound policies persisted longest in Britain, to the detriment of British tank development. Even in the closing stages of the war the primary importance of armament was still not fully recognised for while a new heavy "cruiser" was being designed in 1944, to the A.41 specification, a second, similarly armed but more heavily armoured "infantry" tank, the A.45, was also conceived. However, only the former was produced, as the Centurion, and the doctrine of the two separate, narrowly specialised categories of "cruiser" and "infantry" tanks was finally abandoned in 1946.

Prototypes of the Centurion were built in 1945, just before the end of the war, and in gun-power they compared favourably with other contemporary medium tanks. But they represented no major advance on the German Panther introduced two years earlier. In fact, the two tanks were very similar. For instance, Centurion I weighed 42·5 tons, was powered by a 600 b.h.p. V-12 Rolls-Royce Meteor engine and was armed with a 76·2 mm 17-pounder gun firing armour-piercing shot with a muzzle velocity of 2,950 ft/sec; the Panther, Model D, weighed 43 tons, was powered by a 642 b.h.p. V-12 Maybach engine and was armed with a 75 mm gun with a muzzle velocity of 3,070 ft/sec (Pl. 41).

The post-war development programme adopted in Britain in 1946 centred on a "universal" tank, which was based on the A.45 specification for a more heavily armoured version of the A.41 Centurion. However, the development of the Centurion was also continued and its Mark 3 version was armed with the same 83·4 mm 20-pounder gun as that intended for the "universal" tank. This 1948 development was foreshadowed by the improved version of the Panther which was designed in 1944, but which was never put into production. In its improved form the Panther was to have been armed with the 88 mm gun of the Tiger II, which fired armour-piercing projectiles with a muzzle velocity of 3,340 ft/sec. The 83·4 mm gun mounted in the Centurion had virtually the same performance but it did have one very important advantage over the earlier gun in being provided with a much improved type of armour-piercing discarding sabot, or APDS, ammunition. The latter was fired with a muzzle velocity of 4,800 ft/sec and could penetrate armour almost twice as thick as that which the 88 mm gun penetrated. As a result, Centurion 3 provided the British Army with something it never had before, namely a standard tank better armed than any other.

In its up-gunned form the Centurion was also adopted by several other armies. These included not only the armies of Australia, Canada, India and South Africa, which were then still strongly influenced by the British Army, but also those of Sweden and Switzerland, which ordered their first Centurions in 1953 and 1954, respectively. Egypt and Iraq also acquired some Centurions as, much later, did Israel and the United States purchased a number during the mid-fifties for delivery, under its Military Aid Programmes, to the Netherlands and Denmark. Altogether more than 2,500 Centurions were sold by Britain to other countries, at about £40,000 per vehicle.

As it was being produced, the Centurion was developed further, the Mark 3 being succeeded by the Mark 5 and this being converted into the more heavily armoured Mark 7 (Pl. 42). The most important development was the introduction, in 1959, of the Mark 9, which was a Mark 7 rearmed with a more powerful 105 mm gun (Pl. 43). The new gun was also mounted in the earlier Mark 5 and 8, and it maintained the effectiveness of the Centurion, in face of new developments elsewhere, at least so far as gun-power was concerned. The position was less satisfactory so far as its mobility was concerned as its weight grew to 50 tons with the Mark 3 and 51 tons with the Mark 9.

In the meantime, in 1949, a decision was taken to develop the FV.201 "universal" tank into a 120 mm gun FV.214, or Conqueror (Pl. 44). This was introduced into service in 1954, as a "heavy gun tank" while the Centurion was retained as a "medium gun tank", which implied a two-tank policy of backing the basic medium tanks with a smaller number of more heavily armed tanks. A policy of this kind was followed for years by the Soviet Army, as it had been by the German, and it had nothing to do with the discredited doctrine of "infantry" and "cruiser" tanks, which never differed from each other in armament. Moreover, instead of being kept apart in different units, the two types of tanks were mixed in armoured regiments, there being six Conquerors to forty-two Centurions per regiment.

The role of the Conquerors was to provide heavy fire support for the Centurions, particularly by destroying enemy heavy tanks at long range. Their 120 mm guns, capable of firing APDS at much the same velocity as the 83·4 mm gun of the Centurion, were very suitable for this and, in all probability, the Conquerors outgunned all other contemporary tanks including their potential opponents, the Russian heavy tanks. Unfortunately, in trying to out-armour, as well as to outgun, the Russian tanks, Conquerors became almost as heavy as the German Tiger II and far heavier than any other tank in service. In fact, the Conqueror weighed 65 tons and this seriously reduced its mobility. As a result, within three years of the last one being delivered in 1958 a decision was taken to withdraw them from service. The need for their guns had also decreased as the Centurions were rearmed with the longer-ranged 105 mm guns.

At the time the Conquerors were being withdrawn from British armoured units the Soviety Army was also withdrawing from service its heavy tanks, having, apparently, come to the conclusion that they were more trouble than they were worth, even though they were very considerably lighter than the British tanks. Two tanks were involved in this. One was the IS 3, a 46-ton tank which was first produced just before the end of the war in 1945, but which was not used in action. The other was the T-10, which was superficially similar to the IS 3 and was also armed with a 122 mm gun but which was larger and weighed about 50 tons. The T-10 was first paraded in public in 1957, but by then it had already been in service for three or four years, gradually replacing the IS 3. Both tanks were used, in turn, by the tank divisions of the Soviet Army, to provide heavy fire support for their medium tanks.

For several years after 1945, the basic medium tank remained the T-34/85 (Pl. 45). No less than 11,778 tanks of this type had already been produced in 1944, and after the war it became not only the standard tank of the Soviet Army but also of the Russian-equipped armies of Eastern Europe and of China. An improved version, the T-44, had already been developed before the end of the war but it was not produced in quantity and the T-34/85 was not replaced until the appearance of the T-54. The chassis of the T-54 was developed from that of the

T-44 but it had a much better profiled turret and, what is far more important, a 100 mm gun. In spite of this, it only weighed 36 tons and, therefore, retained the mobility of its predecessors (Pl. 46).

The T-54 was introduced into service around 1953, and was used in numbers by the Soviet armoured formations during the Hungarian uprising of 1956. Subsequently, in 1958–59, it replaced the T-34/85 in Poland and Czechoslovakia, in both of which it has been manufactured under licence, and it was delivered to a number of countries outside the Soviet bloc. Among them was Egypt, which in 1955 received its first T-34/85 tanks, Syria, Iraq and, subsequently, Algeria. The T-54 was also supplied to Finland and Afghanistan, and it was even to be found in the Western Hemisphere, in Cuba, as well as China, which, in turn, supplied tanks of this type to Pakistan in 1966 (Pl. 47). Even then it had not entirely displaced the T-34/85 which was still being used, for instance, by the Egyptian troops in the Yemen. But in the Soviet Army it was already being replaced by the T-62, a tank similar to it but larger, somewhat heavier and armed with a 115 mm gun (Pl. 48).

The T-62 came into service with the Soviet armoured units in 1963, and it sealed the fate of the heavy tanks of the T-10 type which were left with no significant advantage in armament to offset their disadvantages. Their production had already been discontinued and their gradual disappearance coupled with the appearance of the T-62 indicates a concentration on a single type of battle tank as well armed as contemporary technology would allow.

This eminently sound policy was first adopted by the French Army, after tank development was resumed in France towards the end of the Second World War. It manifested itself in the concentration of effort on a single battle tank, the AMX 50, developed by the Atelier de Construction d'Issy-les-Moulineaux, the French Army's armoured vehicle design and development establishment, from whose initials and its target weight of 50 tons it acquired its designation (Pl. 49). The development of the AMX 50 was initiated in 1945, and was strongly influenced by the German Panther and Tiger. In particular, the AMX 50 was intended to combine the mobility of the Panther with the kind of armament which was being considered towards the end of the war for the Tiger. As a result it was armed with a 100 mm gun and was powered by a 1,000 b.h.p. fuel injection engine which originated with the German tanks. The first prototype, which was completed towards the end of 1949, was still armed with a 90 mm gun but within a year it was followed by the 100 mm gun version and in 1952, an even more powerful, 120 mm gun version was built (Pl. 50). Neither version was put into production but the AMX 50 demonstrated the feasibility of a single battle tank as well armed as any other.

In contrast, the U.S. Army subscribed to a policy which called for the development of heavy as well as medium tanks. The policy was formulated in 1946, and led to the design of the 90 mm gun T42 medium and 120 mm gun T43 heavy tanks as successors to the war-time M4A3E8 medium tank with a 76 mm gun and the 90 mm gun M26 heavy tank. But, as before, the U.S. Army did not attach much importance to heavy tanks and the T43 was only produced in small numbers, from 1951 to 1954, as the M103. Moreover, the great majority of the M103 tanks went to the U.S. Marine Corps, in spite of the fact that their weight of 53·5 tons did not make them very suitable for amphibious operations.

The development of the T42, on the other hand, was overtaken by mounting international tension which led to the adoption, in 1948, of an interim model, the M46 medium tank (Pl. 51). The M46 was, basically, the earlier M26 heavy tank with a newly developed engine, transmission and other improvements. Then, in 1950, after the outbreak of the war in Korea, when its own development had not been completed, the turret of the T42 was mounted on the chassis of the M46, to produce another interim model, the M47, Eventually the T42 was abandoned altogether in favour of the M48, which was also armed with a 90 mm gun but which, like the others, was heavier than the T42. In fact, the T42 weighed only 34·3 tons whereas the M47 weighed 43·5 tons and the M48 44·2 tons, or more (Pls. 52–54).

Prototypes of the M48 and its first production models were completed in 1952, and to all intents and purposes it became the sole battle tank of the U.S. Army. As the M48 was produced, the M46 and the M47 were transferred to other armies, under U.S. Military Aid Programmes. The principal recipients of the M46 were the French and Italian armies, which first received it in 1952. Subsequently, they were supplied with much greater quantities of the M47, which was also delivered to Belgium, West Germany, Yugoslavia, Spain, Austria, Greece, Turkey, Persia and Pakistan. In the late fifties, however, the German Army also acquired M48 tanks and by 1965, so had a number of other countries, including Pakistan. Altogether, from mid-1949 to mid-1964, the United States delivered 11,274 medium tanks to other countries, those delivered prior to 1952, being still from the war-time stock of M4 tanks.

In the meantime, the weight of the M48 came to be regarded as excessive and in 1956 the U.S. Army built the prototype of a lighter medium tank, the T95 (Pl. 55). However, before the development of the T95 was completed, a decision was taken to adopt, instead, the M60 (Pl. 56). This was essentially an M48 with a diesel engine and a British-designed 105 mm gun, the same gun, in fact, as that mounted in Centurion 9 but made in the United States. The decision to adopt the M60 was prompted by fears that the M48 tanks were inferior to the Soviet T-54, which had the advantage of being diesel-powered as well as having a larger calibre gun. So far as redressing the advantage in these two respects was concerned the M60 was a success but it was not, in many ways, as good a vehicle as the T95, and it was not lighter than the M48. In fact, its original version weighed 45·5 tons and when it acquired a better turret than that which it had inherited from the M48 its weight grew to 47 tons. This was exactly the same as the weight of its immediate predecessor, the M48A2, whose production continued to the end of 1959, when that of the M60 began.

Dissatisfaction with the relatively heavy tanks developed during the late forties and early fifties was not confined to the United States. In several other countries requirements were also drawn for more mobile battle tanks weighing less than 40 tons and while the United States failed to produce such a tank other countries succeeded. One of them was Switzerland, which had not until then produced any tanks. The Swiss Army had, in fact, recognised the need for a lighter battle tank as early as 1951, when its technical staff began studies which led to such a tank, the Pz. 58 (Pl. 58). The first prototype of this tank was completed in 1958, and like the subsequent pre-production series of ten it was armed with a 90 mm gun. But by 1961 the Swiss Army decided in favour of a more powerful, 105 mm gun and the model which was ordered in that year was not the Pz. 58 but its up-gunned version, the 36·5 ton Pz. 61, armed with the same type of gun as the Centurion 9 but made under licence in Switzerland (Pl. 59). One hundred and fifty Pz. 61 were actually ordered and their delivery commenced in 1964, the production as well as design being accomplished at the Eidgenössische Konstruktionswerkstätte, the Federal military equipment works, at Thun.

An even lighter tank was produced in Japan. Studies leading to it began in 1955 and in the first instance they resulted in the construction of an experimental medium tank, the STA-1. This was the first tank built in Japan since its demilitarisation in 1945 and it was followed by three similar experimental tanks, one of which, the STA-3, was adopted as the Type 61 medium tank (Pl. 57). Like the others, the Type 61 was armed with a 90 mm gun similar to that of the U.S. M48 but it only weighed 34·5 tons. One hundred were ordered from Mitsubishi Nippon Heavy Industries Ltd. and it began to be delivered in 1962.

In the meantime the French Army abandoned the development of the AMX 50, having come to the conclusion that the advantages possessed by such relatively heavily armoured tanks were outweighed by the disadvantages of their heavy weight, particularly when any feasible thickness of armour could be pierced by the warheads of guided missiles and other anti-tank weapons. The AMX 50 was, therefore succeeded by the AMX 38, which weighed about 40 tons. But the AMX 38 also failed to advance beyond the prototype stage, as it was displaced by an even lighter tank, the AMX 30.

The AMX 30 was developed to a tripartite specification agreed to in 1957, by France, Germany and Italy. Its first two prototypes were completed in 1960, and although it was armed with a 105 mm gun its weight was only 32 tons. Between the construction of a pre-production series of seven in 1961 and the appearance of the first production model in 1966, the weight increased to 33·5 tons but even then the AMX 30 was the lightest and, all-round, the most mobile battle tank of its generation. However, of the three armies which were originally involved in its development, only the French adopted the AMX 30 (Pls. 60 and 61).

The German Army adopted, instead, the Leopard, developed in Germany to the same 1957 tripartite specification as the AMX 30. The first two prototypes of the Leopard, or *Standardpanzer* as it was originally called, were completed in 1961. They were the first German tanks to be built since 1945, when Germany was not only prohibited from having tanks, as she was after 1918, by the Treaty of Versailles, but also from having any armed forces at all and the tank development facilities were completely destroyed. In consequence, when the German Army began to be re-created in 1956, the development of tanks re-started, virtually, from scratch. In spite of this, by the end of 1962, enough pre-production vehicles were built to equip a tank company for extensive troop trials. In 1963 the Leopard was officially adopted in preference to the AMX 30, a year later an order was placed for about 1,400 and in September 1965 the Krauss-Maffei Company completed the first production vehicle. By then the weight of the Leopard had grown to 39·5 tons but while it is heavier and larger than the AMX 30 it has at least as much horse power per ton, due to its powerful 830 b.h.p. Daimler Benz V-10 engine. In gun-power, on the other hand, the Leopard is similar to Centurion 9, as it has the same British-made 105 mm gun, and by the same token to the U.S. M60 and the Swiss Pz. 61. (Pls. 62 and 63).

Italy also opted out of the 1957 tripartite agreement to develop a single "European" battle tank and adopted, in 1965, the U.S. M60 as a successor to its U.S. built M47 medium tanks. The M60 had by then become a very attractive proposition, not only because it was well proved but, even more, because the U.S. Army was prepared to sell it below cost price—at about £65,000, in fact, instead of the cost price of £71,000, which already compared favourably with the cost of £85,000 for the Leopard and the even higher costs of other tanks. The reason behind this was the fact that the U.S. Army already had all the M60 tanks it needed but, rightly, did not want to close down its battle tank production facilities until the introduction of the next model and, in the circumstances, it was more economical to sell tanks at a loss than not to produce any M60 tanks at all. However, only about 20 per cent of the total number of M60 tanks to be procured by the Italian Army were to come directly from the United States: the rest were to be assembled in Italy, partly from Italian and partly from American-made components, under a "co-production" scheme.

Apart from the AMX 30 and the Leopard, the Italian Army also had the opportunity, which was not taken up, of adopting one of two British tanks. One was the 37-ton battle tank developed by Vickers Ltd. for the Indian Army, as a result of an agreement reached in 1961. The first prototype of this tank was completed in 1963, and was followed by the production of a batch in England but the agreement envisaged that it would be produced in quantity at a factory built for the purpose near Madras, where assembly from British-made components did start in 1966. The design of the Vickers 37-ton battle tank or, to give it its Indian name, "Vijayanta" was derived from that of the FV. 300, a light tank designed in the late forties to a British Army requirement but never developed beyond the prototype stage. Its general characteristics are, however, closest to those of the Leopard and it is armed with the same 105 mm gun. (Pl. 64).

The second of the two British tanks was the Chieftain, which originated with a War Office specification issued in 1957, and which differed from other contemporary designs in two very important respects. First, it had a larger, 120 mm gun. Secondly, it was considerably heavier than most other battle tanks (Pl. 65).

The reason why the Chieftain has come to have a larger calibre gun is, basically, that the British General Staff became convinced of the need to fight enemy tanks at longer ranges than those envisaged by others. Thus, while the maximum effective range demanded, for instance, of U.S.

tanks was of the order of 2,000 metres, that of British tanks rose well above it, although historical evidence and terrain studies showed that in the great majority of cases tanks sighted other tanks at ranges below that specified for the U.S. tanks. The reason why the Chieftain is heavier than all other battle tanks is that it is more heavily armoured and this, in turn, is due to the importance which has continued to be attached in Britain to armour protection, particularly from the point of view of tank versus tank battles. As a result, official policies have been couched in terms of a "gun-armour combination" and the Chieftain has come to weigh 51 tons. Originally it had been hoped that it would weigh no more than 45 tons but even then the Chieftain represented different ideas from those which prevailed in almost all other countries, where mobility was considered more important than armour protection.

In one respect, however, the Chieftain resembled its contemporaries, namely in being developed as a single type of battle tank, and it was intended to replace both the Centurion and the Conqueror. But by the time the first production vehicle was finally built in mid-1965, the Conqueror had been withdrawn from service and British armoured units were already using only one type of tank, the 105 mm gun Centurion, which the Chieftain began to replace towards the end of 1966.

An entirely different type of tank has been adopted in Sweden. Like the Swiss, the Swedish Army decided during the early fifties to develop a modern battle tank of its own instead of importing more tanks from Britain, or elsewhere. The design which was consequently produced to its requirements by the Landsverk Company was fairly conventional, except for being armed with a 150 mm gun. But this relatively heavy tank had not advanced beyond the prototype stage when in 1956 the chief engineer of the Vehicle Division of the Swedish Army Ordnance, S. Berge, proposed an entirely different solution. This amounted to a turretless tank with a fixed gun mounting, which became the object of feasibility studies and, after their successful completion in 1958, led to an order being given to the Bofors Company to develop such a vehicle. As a result, two prototypes of what has since been called the S-tank, or Strv 103, were built by the winter of 1962–1963, and after trials the Swedish Army decided to adopt it, placing a production order with Bofors in mid-1964. In spite of its novel features, the first production models of the S-tank were completed in 1966, and in the meantime a pre-production series of ten had also been built (Pls. 66 and 67).

The adoption of a turretless layout has given the S-tank a much lower silhouette than that of other, more conventional tanks and this, in turn, has given it a greater chance of surviving in battle. The absence of a turret did not, in itself, represent anything new. Turretless vehicles were used on a large scale during the Second World War by the German and Soviet Armies and although their importance subsequently declined both armies have developed new vehicles of this type, for special purposes. The principal Russian vehicle is the ASU-85, a light air-transportable 85 mm assault gun introduced around 1961; the German vehicle is the *Jagdpanzer* (*Kanone*), a 90 mm gun tank destroyer ordered in 1960 (Pl. 69). The design of the S-tank represents, however, a considerable advance on these and the earlier turretless vehicles as a result of the adoption of the fixed gun mounting. This logical step has eliminated the need for the space required hitherto within the armour envelope by the movement of the breech end of the gun. It has also made it possible to install a relatively simple automatic loading mechanism, since there is no movement between the breech and the ammunition magazine. In turn, this has made it possible to dispense with the human loader and thus save a considerable amount of space within the tank, making it more compact still. Moreover, the provision of an automatic loader together with the simplification of driving and gunnery controls makes it possible, in an emergency, for one man to operate the S-tank, though normally it is manned by a crew of three.

The adoption of the fixed gun mounting has meant that the gun can only be elevated or depressed by altering the pitch of the hull, by means of an adjustable hydropneumatic suspension. Similarly, the gun can only be traversed by turning the whole vehicle, which means that the S-tank can not move in one direction and fire its main armament in another. The importance of this is, however, questionable since all tanks must stop to fire accurately and the S-tank can stop and engage a surprise target at least as quickly as a conventional tank.

In spite of all the differences, the S-tank is similar to other contemporary tanks in some respects, including its 105 mm gun main armament and a weight of 36·5 tons. The gun is, however, longer barrelled and its relatively light weight does not imply that the S-tank is lightly armoured because its shape and size have made it possible to combine a high degree of frontal protection with reasonable vehicle weight.

Another departure from previously accepted practice is represented by the M60A1E1, the standard U.S. battle tank rearmed with a 152 mm gun/launcher capable of firing Shillelagh guided missiles as well as conventional shells (Pl. 70). A similar type of main armament has also been proposed for the U.S. German MBT-70, the main battle tank which is being developed under an agreement signed by the United States and Germany in 1963 and which is to replace the M60 and the Leopard. In the meantime, the M60A1E1 has been introduced to supplement the 105 mm gun armed M60A1.

The new type of armament mounted in the M60A1E1 originated with the M551 Sheridan, an Armoured Reconnaissance/Airborne Assault Vehicle (Pl. 71), and this, in turn, followed from several earlier attempts at the development of an air-transportable light tank. The first dates back to 1941, when the U.S. Army started work on the T9 light tank. The development of the T9 was not, however, matched by that of an aircraft to carry it and when it was built, as the M22 light tank, the only aircraft capable of carrying it was the British Hamilcar glider. Consequently only a few M22 were finally used by the British 6th Airborne Division at the crossing of the Rhine, in March 1945, and the first tanks to go into action by air were seven British Tetrarch light tanks, landed by Hamilcar gliders on D-Day in Normandy in 1944 (Pl. 72 and 73).

Aircraft capable of carrying the 7-ton M22 became available after the war but its military value had become negligible, as it was only armed with a 37 mm gun. To replace the M22, as well as the M24, which was built mainly for reconnaissance, the U.S. Army produced the M41 light tank. This 76 mm gun model, originally called the T41, was conceived in 1946 together with the T42 medium and T43 heavy tanks and it was put into production in 1950. Unfortunately, it weighed 22·8 tons, which made it far too heavy for airborne use. At the same time it was too large for a good reconnaisance vehicle, although it has been used as such not only by the U.S. Army but also by the German, Italian and other armies.

The French Army was more successful in developing an air-transportable light tank, the AMX 13, work on which also began in 1946 (Pl. 74). The original idea that it would be flown about the French overseas possessions was far-fetched, but no more so than many other ideas on airborne tanks and, as it only weighed 14·3 tons, it could at least be carried by the contemporary Breguet *Deux Ponts* transport aircraft (Pl. 75). However, the *Deux Ponts* was never put into production and, instead of being an airborne tank, the AMX 13 became a tank destroyer, for which its high-velocity 75 mm gun made it very suitable. The gun was, in fact, comparable to that of the German Panther and when its prototype appeared in 1949, the AMX 13 was as well armed as the contemporary medium tanks. At the same time it had the advantage of being very considerably lighter and more mobile. In consequence, it represented a very effective type of vehicle and was produced, from 1952 onwards, not only for the French Army but also fourteen others. Among them are the Israeli Army, which successfully used the AMX 13 during the 1956 Sinai campaign, and the armies of countries as far afield as India or Indonesia and Venezuela or Peru, as well as Switzerland, Austria and the Netherlands.

A prototype of the AMX 13 was also tested in 1951 in the United States where work began a year later on a somewhat similar T92 light tank, which was intended to be an air-transportable replacement for the M41. Like the M41, the T92 was armed with a 76 mm gun but it weighed 16 tons, and was also smaller, which made it much more attractive. However, although prototypes were built in 1956 and 1957, the T92 was not adopted, as tanks of this type no longer met the requirements of reconnaissance and airborne operations (Pl. 77).

The requirements of reconnaissance and airborne operations were not easy to meet in a single vehicle and the Soviet Army was relatively more successful in developing the PT-76 light tank purely as a reconnaissance vehicle. As an amphibian, the PT-76 can trace its ancestry, through the T-40, T-38 and T-37 amphibious light tanks, to the A.4 E.11 of 1930, which was by far the most sensible version of the Vickers-Carden-Loyd light tanks. Like them, it sacrificed armament to mobility and its utility is limited to reconnaissance but because of its ability to cross inland water obstacles without preparation it is more mobile overall than other light tanks and is, therefore, more effective as a reconnaissance vehicle. At 14 tons it is also light enough to be carried by air but its amphibious characteristics make it too bulky for an efficient airborne tank and its 76 mm gun is not powerful enough for it to be an airborne assault vehicle. It was, therefore, solely as a reconnaissance vehicle that the PT-76 came into service with the Soviet Army around 1952. Since then it has also been used elsewhere, from Poland through Afghanistan to Laos (Pl. 78).

In contrast, the U.S. Army has developed the M551 Sheridan to fulfil the role of an airborne tank as well as a reconnaissance vehicle. This has, inevitably, involved compromises between conflicting requirements and, in consequence, the Sheridan is not as good an amphibian as the PT-76. It is also costly for a reconnaissance vehicle. But its main armament of the 152 mm gun/launcher is well in advance of all other light tanks. In fact, because of the accuracy as well as size of the Shillelagh guided missiles which it can fire, the Sheridan has an armament superior in some respects to the 105 mm guns of contemporary battle tanks, although it weighs only 14·8 tons.

The development which has led to this started in 1959 and centred on the Shillelagh guided missile, for which the Aeronutronic Division of the Ford Motor Company was mainly responsible. The vehicle, on the other hand, was developed at the U.S. Army Cleveland tank plant operated first by the Cadillac and then the Allison Division of the General Motors Corporation. Trials with prototypes started in 1962 and the first production vehicle was completed four years later, in June 1966. The relatively short period of development was a considerable achievement in view of the novel nature of the armament of the Sheridan and its appearance marked another important step in the evolution of the tank.

CHAPTER 3

Tank Weapons

SINCE tanks are, in essence, mobile weapon platforms, their design centres on armament. In fact, armament not only provides a focal point but governs much of the design of tanks, which are little more than carriers for the chosen weapons.

The choice of weapons mounted in tanks is dictated by their potential targets and if they are not to be confined to a limited role they must be able to engage more than one type. Up to the middle of the Second World War this requirement was generally met by medium-velocity 75 or 76 mm guns mounted in combination with rifle-calibre machine guns. Guns of this type were already mounted in the very first French tanks and they fired shells large enough to be effective against a wide variety of battlefield targets, including contemporary tanks. For a time, in fact, even low-velocity guns of this calibre were adequate. Thus, the German Pz. Kpfw. IV had a 75 mm gun which was 24 calibres long and fired armour piercing shells with a muzzle velocity of only 1,260 ft/sec, while the Russian T-28 and T-35 had even shorter, 16·5 calibre 76·2 mm guns, whereas the gun of the French Saint-Chamond of 1916 was already 36 calibres long and had a muzzle velocity of 1,800 ft/sec.

But as the armour of tanks grew in thickness, higher muzzle velocities and, therefore, longer-barrelled guns became necessary. In consequence, the later versions of the Russian T-28 were armed with 76·2 mm guns 26 calibres long and the T-34 and KV tanks were armed with guns of the same calibre but 30·5 and then 41·5 calibres long. Similarly, the barrel length of the 75 mm guns mounted in U.S. medium tanks grew from 31 calibres in the case of the M3 to 40 in the case of the M4, while the German Pz. Kpfw. IV was rearmed with 43 and then 48 calibre long guns.

In combination with machine guns, the 75 or 76·2 mm guns of the M4, T-34 and Pz. Kpfw. IV satisfied for a time all requirements. In particular, they fired armour piercing projectiles of about 15 lb. with muzzle velocities ranging from 2,050 to 2,450 ft/sec, which made them effective against the armour of the contemporary tanks, and they also fired high explosive shells which were large enough to be effective against various unarmoured targets. However, as the armour of tanks increased still further in thickness, the armour-piercing performance of these guns became inadequate.

The consequent problem of developing guns capable of defeating thicker armour is best seen in the light of what is needed for an armour-piercing projectile to perforate armour plate. The mechanics of perforation are complex but, in essence, the process amounts to equating the kinetic energy of the projectile to the work done while it penetrates and ultimately perforates the target plate. Moreover, the perforating ability of a projectile can be adequately described by an empirical equation, which corresponds to de Marre's 19th-century formula:

$$wv^2 = kd^3\left(\frac{t}{d}\right)^n \qquad (3.1)$$

where w = weight of projectile, lb
v = velocity of projectile, ft/sec
d = diameter of projectile, in
t = thickness of plate which the projectile only just perforates, in
k = constant depending on the projectile and the target plate.

The index n has a value of about 1·4, which makes the observed results lie between the theoretical equations for the projectile penetrating armour against a constant pressure, interpreted as the hydrostatic pressure necessary to expand a cylindrical hole in the target plate by moving the material sideways, and for the projectile pushing out a cylindrical plug in the presence of a constant shear stress at the surface of the plug; in the first case $n = 1$ and in the second $n = 2$.

The constant k is approximately equal to 10^6 for typical projectiles and armour plates. This means that a conventional armour-piercing, or AP, shot or shell with an muzzle velocity of 2,000 ft/sec can perforate armour 1·3 times as thick as its diameter, when it strikes the armour normal to its surface and at point blank range. For a muzzle velocity of 2,600 ft/sec the ratio of the thickness of armour which the AP shot can perforate to its own diameter goes up to about 1·8 and for 3,500 ft/sec to 2·8.

Improved armour-piercing performance can, therefore, be obtained either by increasing the muzzle velocity of the AP shot or by increasing its diameter, by going to a larger calibre gun, since for a given velocity the larger the diameter the greater the thickness of the armour which can be perforated. The best example of the first approach is provided by the German Panther, which was armed with a gun of the same 75 mm calibre as its predecessors but with a longer, 70-calibre barrel and a muzzle velocity of 3,070 ft/sec. A good example of the second approach is provided by the Russian IS tank, armed with a gun whose length of 43 calibres and muzzle velocity of 2,580 ft/sec were not very different from those of the earlier 75 or 76·2 mm guns but which had a calibre of 122 mm.

But, if either approach could lead to the desired improvement in penetration at short range, large calibre, low velocity guns have an advantage over small calibre, high velocity guns because the performance of their projectiles falls off less rapidly with range. The fall-off in the performance is due to aerodynamic drag which progressively reduces the velocity of the projectiles, the drop per unit distance increasing with the ratio of the frontal area of the projectile to its weight, as well as its velocity and form factor or drag coefficient. The frontal area of the projectile is, in turn, proportional to the square of its diameter while its weight is proportional to the diameter cubed. In consequence, the ratio of frontal area to weight decreases as the diameter of the projectile increases, so that the large-calibre projectiles lose their velocity less rapidly with distance. This made increases in gun calibre more attractive, particularly as the range at which tanks began to engage other tanks increased during the later part of the Second World War.

The best performance was, of course, bound to come from a combination of the largest possible calibre with the highest possible muzzle velocity. A move towards such a combination was clearly represented by the German Tiger II, which had an 88 mm gun with a muzzle velocity of 3,340 ft/sec. It was also represented by the turretless Jagdtiger, which had a 128 mm gun with a muzzle velocity of 3,020 ft/sec and was the most powerfully armed vehicle introduced up to the end of the Second World War. In fact, between them, the Tiger II and the Jagdtiger came close to the limit of calibre and muzzle velocity so far as guns firing conventional, full-bore AP projectiles were concerned. Attempts at increasing the velocity of such projectiles still further run up against the law of diminishing returns, as they involved disproportionate increases in chamber pressure, weight of propellant, barrel length and rate of bore wear. Conventional AP rounds of 120 mm, or so, were also heavy and difficult to manhandle within tank turrets. Two-piece ammunition, with a separate projectile and case, has had to be used, therefore, and the longer time required to load the separated ammunition has meant a slower rate of fire. The size of the projectile and case also limited the number of rounds which could be stowed in the tank. For example, the Tiger II still carried 84 rounds of 88 mm ammunition but the U.S. M103 could only accommodate 34 rounds for its 120 mm gun and the Russian IS 3 the even smaller number of 28 rounds. Moreover, the firing of conventional 120 mm AP projectiles with high muzzle velocities involves very large reaction forces on the vehicle.

The magnitude of the forces which arise when tank guns are fired can be determined by equating the momenta of the projectile and the propellant gases to the momentum of the recoiling mass of the gun and then equating the kinetic energy of the recoiling mass to the work done in bringing it to rest. Thus, the average force F on the trunnions of the gun is given, to a first approximation, by the equation:

$$F = \frac{(w_p v_p + w_c v_c)^2}{2 g w_G L} \quad (3.2)$$

where w_p = weight of projectile
w_c = weight of propellant
w_G = weight of recoiling mass of gun
v_p = muzzle velocity of projectile
v_c = escape velocity of propellant gases
L = length of recoil
g = acceleration due to gravity.

Equation (3.2) shows that the trunnion forces are inversely proportional to the weight of the gun and the length of recoil. From the point of view of minimising the forces it would be desirable, therefore, to have a fairly heavy gun and long recoil but the first is undesirable because of its effect on overall vehicle weight and the second is severely restricted by the limited space available in tank turrets.

The effect of projectile weight and velocity is best shown by substituting some typical figures in equation (3.2). These, for a 120 mm gun, might be 50, 29·5 and 6,400 lb for the weight of the projectile, propellant charge and recoiling mass of the gun respectively; 1·06 ft for the length of recoil and 3,500 ft/sec for the muzzle velocity of the projectile while 4,700 ft/sec is the average velocity with which propellant gases escape from gun barrels. When these figures are substituted in the equation the average force comes to no less than 100 tons. Forces of this magnitude have been considered unacceptable for conventional tanks of around 50 tons and it was only after the installation of muzzle brakes, which reduced the average force to about 70 tons, that the ammunition considered has been fired from them.

For all this even larger calibre guns have been considered for tanks. For instance, 150 mm guns were considered in Germany, in 1944, for the Maus and E.100 experimental super-heavy tanks and in 1947 the U.S. Army actually built the T30 experimental heavy tank with a 155 mm gun. However, in view of all the difficulties with 120 mm guns, it is not surprising that larger guns were not adopted, although some more experimental large-gun tanks were built during the fifties, including an experimental Centurion with a 183 mm gun.

Instead, attention turned from the original, full-bore, monobloc, steel AP projectiles to other types of armour-piercing projectiles. One of them was the armour-piercing, composite, rigid, or APCR, shot, which consists of a hard, high-density, core in a soft, low-density jacket and which is lighter than a conventional AP projectile of the same calibre. In consequence, its muzzle velocity is higher and although its kinetic energy at the muzzle may not be different from that of the AP shot fired from the same gun, it can perforate thicker armour because it creates a smaller diameter hole, since penetration is confined to the sub-calibre core, which separates on impact from the soft jacket. In other words, the APCR shot concentrates the available kinetic energy on a smaller area of the target and less of this energy is, therefore, dissipated per unit depth of penetration than in the case of the full-calibre AP projectiles, so that its total penetration is greater. To achieve this, cores of APCR projectiles need to be made of high-density materials and this has led to the use of tungsten carbide cemented by cobalt. The combination of tungsten carbide with about 25 per cent of cobalt, produced by sintering them in powder form, gives a tough material having a density of 13 g/cm^3, compared with 7.85 for steel. More recently even heavier metals have been developed for armour-piercing projectiles in the form of sintered tungsten alloys having densities of 16·9 to 17, or even 18·5 g/cm^3.

APCR projectiles suffer, however, from the disadvantage that their velocity and, therefore, their armour piercing performance fall off rapidly with range. The fall-off in performance is illustrated in Fig. 1, which shows the penetration vs. range of the conventional, armour-piercing, capped, and ballistically capped, or APCBC, and APCR projectiles fired from the 71-calibre long 88 mm gun of the Tiger II; the

APCBC projectile weighed 22·25 lb and had a muzzle velocity of 3,340 ft/sec, the corresponding figures for the APCR being 16 and 3,700 ft/sec. The cause of the greater fall-off in the performance of the APCR projectile was its higher velocity and, even more, that it had the same frontal area as the APCBC projectile while being considerably lighter.

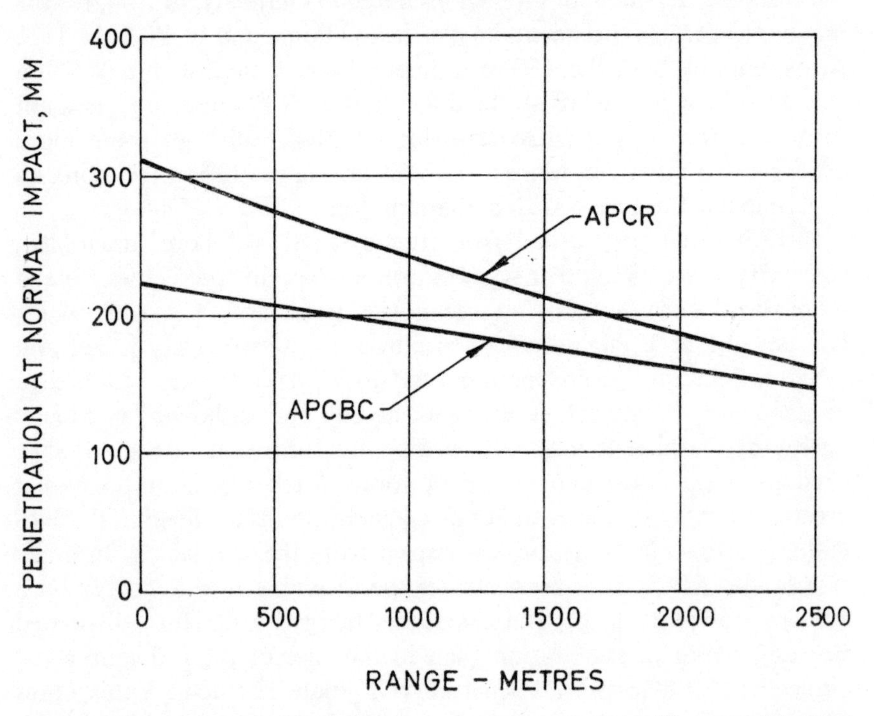

Fig. 1 Armour penetration versus range of APCBC and APCR projectiles fired from the German 88 mm L/71 gun.

In other words, it had a higher ratio of frontal area to weight and suffered more from aerodynamic drag, for the reasons stated earlier. More frequently the same thing is expressed in terms of the ratio of weight to area, or "sectional density", or, more generally, in terms of the "ballistic coefficient", which is equal to the sectional density divided by the form factor. Thus, the higher the ballistic coefficient of a projectile the less does its velocity decrease with distance.

In spite of its low ballistic coefficient, APCR ammunition has been used successfully with a number of tank guns, starting in 1941 with the 50 mm gun of the German Pz. Kpfw. III. Since then it has also been used with Russian and American tank guns, including the 76 mm gun of the M41 tank and the 90 mm gun of the M48. In the United States it is called "hyper-velocity armour-piercing", or HVAP, and its velocity has been raised to 4,100 ft/sec, in the case of the 76 mm gun projectiles. APCR ammunition has not been used, however, by the British Army which adopted, instead, the armour-piercing, discarding-sabot, or APDS, type. The APDS was, in many ways, the logical development of the APCR from which it differed mainly in the separation of the core from the outer body after leaving the muzzle. Thus, in contrast to the APCR, where the whole projectile travels to the target, only the core does so in the case of the APDS and its ballistic coefficient is not only much higher than that of the APCR projectiles but higher even than that of the APCBC type. In consequence, the armour-piercing performance of the APDS is greatly superior to that of the APCR at longer ranges.

At short ranges there is relatively little to choose between them, given the same muzzle velocity and core size, and their ability to penetrate armour can be estimated, like that of other projectiles, from equation (3.1). For a typical APDS shot having a muzzle velocity of 4,800 ft/sec the thickness of armour which it can just perforate at normal impact and point-blank range comes to about 7 times the diameter of the core or to about 4 times the calibre of the shot. The penetrating ability of the APDS shot is, therefore, very considerable and far greater than that of the earlier types of armour-piercing projectiles. However, the APDS shot also has some drawbacks. For instance disturbances arising during the separation of the core from the sabot increase its dispersion and the discarded elements constitute a hazard to own troops if APDS is fired over their heads. Nevertheless, APDS ammunition has come to be used to an increasing extent.

The APDS shot was first used in 1944, with the 57 mm 6-pounder guns, which were then still used in the Churchill infantry tanks. By the end of 1944, it was also produced for the 76·2 mm 17-pounder. Its muzzle velocity at that stage was 3,950 ft/sec, which meant an increase of 1,000 ft/sec over the conventional APCBC shot fired from the 17-pounder and was comparable with that of contemporary APCR shots. Subsequent development increased its muzzle velocity still further and the 83·4 mm 20-pounder introduced in 1948, fired APDS projectiles with a muzzle velocity of 4,800 ft/sec. So does the 105 mm gun which has been adopted for the U.S. M60, the German Leopard and the Swiss Pz.61, as well as the British Centurions.

Still higher velocities have been obtained with experimental smooth-bore guns firing fin-, instead of spin-stabilised, projectiles. They include 120 mm tank guns developed during the fifties in the United States and their potentialities are indicated by smooth-bore high-velocity guns used since 1960 in the United States for high altitude research. One of them is a 16 in. naval gun converted to a 16·5 in. smooth-bore which can fire 400 lb fin-stabilised, sub-calibre projectiles with a muzzle velocity of 6,000 ft/sec, instead of the original 3,000 lb full-bore, spin-stabilised shells fired at 2,800 ft/sec.

Even this, however, has been improved upon in experiments carried out during the early sixties at the Canadian Armament Research and Development Establishment, at Valcartier, Quebec. The experiments were based on a 76·2 mm 17-pounder, which in its original form fired 17 lb full-bore projectiles at 2,950 ft/sec and 7·6 lb APDS shots at 3,950 ft/sec; when the rifling was removed the same gun proved capable of firing 1 lb sub-calibre projectiles at 7,000 ft/sec and when a second smooth-bore barrel was attached to the first, to give a total barrel length of 100 instead of 50 calibres, it fired the same 1 lb projectile at 9,150 ft/sec.

Considerable increases in the muzzle velocity of tank guns are, therefore, feasible but they do not, necessarily, imply corresponding increases in the penetration of armour-piercing projectiles. At high impact velocities cavitation sets in, so that conical instead of cylindrical holes are produced in the armour plate, and more energy is dissipated for a given depth of penetration. Moreover, as the velocities increase so does the intensity of the stress waves initiated in the projectiles on impact, until a limit is reached when projectiles made of the available materials begin to shatter. Increases in muzzle velocity also offer the advantage of flatter projectile trajectories and, therefore, increase the chances of hitting targets but this has tended to be nullified by the greater dispersion of the fin-stabilised projectiles.

There is no doubt, however, about the improvements in the performance of armour-piercing ammunition due to the increases in muzzle velocity which have already taken place with APDS projectiles. These increases have also made it possible to keep the weight of armour-piercing rounds within reasonable limits, because improved performance has been achieved with lighter projectiles. In fact, the weight of an APDS shot is only about half that of an APCBC projectile of the same calibre while its penetration is much greater. But when the demands for penetrating progressively thicker armour at ever longer ranges push the gun calibre to 120 mm, even APDS rounds have to be of the separated type to ease manhandling, as shown by the Conqueror and the Chieftain. Moreover, even with APDS ammunition, the recoil forces of 120 mm guns are such that they can only be mounted in relatively heavy vehicles (Pl. 80).

The alternative is to use ammunition which does not rely for penetrating armour on the kinetic energy of the projectiles but on the focused blast energy of their explosive content. This means projectiles with shaped, or hollow, charges, usually referred to as HEAT, or "high-explosive, anti-tank". Projectiles of this kind penetrate armour by virtue of having a copper-lined conical cavity in their explosive charge which, on detonation, produces a very high-velocity jet of copper whose impact generates extremely high pressures. The velocities of standard shaped charge jets are, in fact, of the order of 27,000 ft/sec and this produces pressures at the point of impact which are very much greater than the yield stresses of armour. In consequence the target, as well as the jet, materials are assumed to behave like perfect fluids, so that the mechanics of penetration can be considered in hydrodynamic terms and described by Bernoulli's equation. This leads to an equation for the total depth of penetration,

$$t = L\sqrt{\frac{\rho_j}{\rho_a}} \tag{3.3}$$

where L = effective length of the jet
ρ_j = density of the jet
ρ_a = density of the target material.

Thus, for a given shaped charge, the depth of penetration is inversely proportional to the square root of the density of the target material. For a given target material, on the other hand, the depth of penetration depends on the length and density of the jet but not on its velocity. In practice, however, the jet must possess a certain minimum velocity if it is to penetrate the target and for normal steel armour this is of the order of 8,000 ft/sec.

Equation (3.3) is useful for comparing the relative effectiveness of different materials as protection against shaped charges but it cannot be used to predict penetration, because L, the length of the jet, is difficult to determine. Penetration is, therefore, generally predicted from empirical data which relate it to the base diameter of the conical liner and the stand-off—the distance from the base of the charge to the surface of the target. The dependence of penetration on these two parameters is indicated in Fig. II, where it is plotted in terms of cone diameters against stand-off, also in terms of cone diameters, for a standard and a precision-made shaped charges. In both cases there is an optimum stand-off, above which penetration decreases with increasing stand-off. The most noteworthy fact, however, is that a

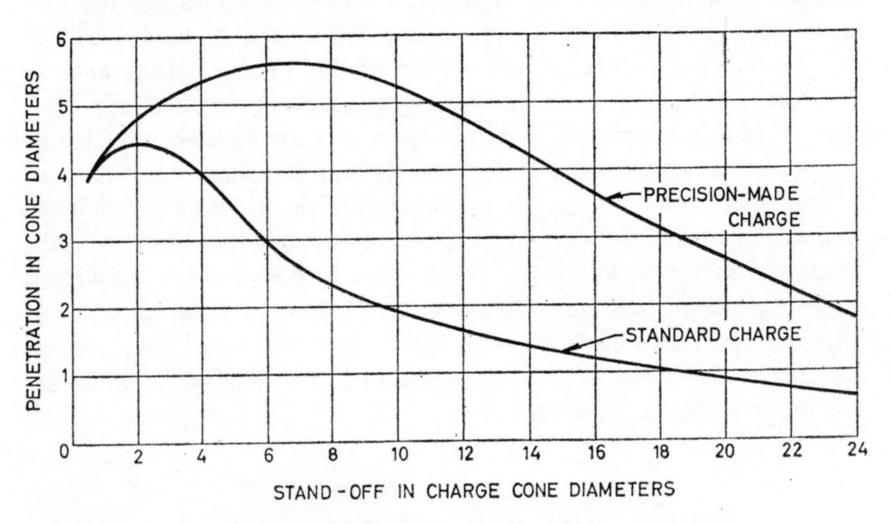

Fig. II Armour penetration of shaped charges versus stand-off distance.

precision made charge can penetrate normal steel armour to a depth equivalent to about 5·6 cone diameters. When an allowance is made for the thickness of the walls of the shells containing the shaped charge, the penetration at optimum stand-off becomes equal to between 3·5 to 4 times the calibre of the shell. But even then the penetration of shaped charge shells compares favourably with that of other armour-piercing projectiles.

What is required, however, of armour-piercing projectiles is not merely that they should perforate armour but they should cause lethal damage behind it. In this respect shaped charges are relatively less effective, since they produce holes which decrease in diameter with the depth of penetration and which may not be large enough at exit to be lethal unless the maximum penetration capability of the shaped charge exceeds to a considerable extent the thickness of the armour it perforates. In contrast, a perforation by an APDS projectile implies immediately a high degree of lethal damage as it involves the penetration of armour by a heavy shot. The most lethal of all are APHE shells, that is AP projectiles with a small bursting charge which explodes after penetration, but the thickness of armour they can penetrate is even lower than that of AP shot, because of their lower sectional density and weaker structure.

To ensure an adequate degree of lethality shaped charge shells must, therefore, be larger than necessary to perforate a given thickness of armour and, on the face of it, compare less favourably with other armour-piercing projectiles. But although shaped charge projectiles need to be of relatively large calibre this is far less of a problem than with other types of projectiles because they are light in relation to their size and need not be fired at high velocities.

The light weight of shaped charges in relation to their performance and the fact that they need not be fired at high velocities has made them the basis of several portable infantry anti-tank weapons, from anti-tank rifle grenades, through rocket launchers, such as the U.S. 2·36 in. "bazooka" of 1942, to the more recent 84 mm Carl Gustav recoilless gun. Some of the heavier anti-tank recoilless guns have also been mounted in light armoured vehicles. Examples of this are provided by the Ontos with six 106 mm guns, which was adopted in 1956 by the U.S. Marine Corps (Pl. 81), and the Japanese SS with two 106 mm guns. The combination of a large-calibre recoilless gun firing shaped charge projectiles with a light armoured vehicle has been attractive but it did not extend beyond the Ontos and the SS, mainly because recoilless guns require at least twice as much propellant as conventional guns of similar performance and their ammunition is, therefore, bulky and heavy. Moreover, their back-blast constitutes a hazard to own troops and makes them conspicuous when they fire.

By comparison with infantry anti-tank weapons, the application of shaped charges to tank guns has been slow, even though HEAT shells were introduced as early as 1942, for the short 75 mm gun which was then still mounted in the German Pz. Kpfw. IV. One of the obstacles to the use of shaped charges with tank guns has been the reduction of their armour penetration when they are incorporated in conventional, spin-stabilised projectiles. The very high rates of spin of such projectiles and the fact that the liner material flows radially inwards when the charge is exploded while conserving its angular momentum lead to very high angular velocities of the shaped charge jet and this tends to break it up, reducing penetration by up to 50 per cent. In consequence, before shaped charges could be used effectively with tank guns, new types of projectiles had to be developed. The most obvious were unspun, fin-stabilised projectiles but their dispersion tended to be considerable and it was only relatively recently that a satisfactory projectile of this type with an ingenious blunt nose configuration was developed in the United States for 90 and 105 mm tank guns. However, fin-stabilised HEAT ammunition is now used in the U.S. M60 and the German Leopard in addition to the British-developed APDS ammunition.

An entirely different type of HEAT projectile has been developed in France for the AMX 30 and the upgunned, 105 mm gun, version of the AMX 13. It is spin-stabilised but degradation of the performance of the shaped charge is prevented by mounting it in ball bearings so that it does not rotate with the projectile body. The double-shell construction implies some reduction in the shaped charge diameter but, nevertheless, the 105 mm HEAT projectile of AMX 30 can penetrate 400 mm of armour. Moreover, its penetration, like that of other HEAT projectiles, does not fall-off with range and it is used in the AMX 30 to the exclusion of other types of armour-piercing projectiles.

In Britain, on the other hand, no serious attempt has been made to develop HEAT rounds and both the American and French projectiles have been decried on the grounds of accuracy and lethality. Instead, APDS ammunition has been preferred in Britain, as well as Sweden and Switzerland. The APDS projectiles certainly have an advantage over HEAT projectiles in their higher velocity and higher ballistic coefficients, which imply a flatter trajectory and, therefore, make the probability of hitting targets less sensitive to errors in elevation arising from inaccurate estimates of the ranges of targets. The HEAT projectiles of the AMX 30 are, in fact, fired with a muzzle velocity of 3,300 ft/sec and the U.S. 90 mm HEAT projectiles have an even higher velocity of 4,000 ft/sec. But this is still lower than the muzzle velocity of APDS shot, and so is the ballistic coefficient of all HEAT projectiles. However, the consequent differences in the chances of hitting targets can be largely eliminated by the use of more sophisticated fire control systems with range finders and ballistic computers.

As early as 1945, a turret was developed in Germany for the Panther which incorporated a stereoscopic range finder, as well as the 88 mm gun of the Tiger II. After the war, in 1946, the U.S. Army went further and specified range finders for all three tanks which it decided to develop, the T41, T42 and T43. The choice again fell on the stereoscopic type, mounted right across the turret. However, when the stereoscopic range finders came into service in the M47, and then the M48 and M103, tanks they proved to require an inordinate amount of training, as well as preliminary selection of tank crewmen since not all can use it. Moreover, experience showed that the stereoscopic range finders failed to be fully used in the field. As a result, a simpler, full-field coincidence, or superposition type of range finder was installed in the M48A3 and the M60, in spite of the fact that it absorbs more light, which limits its use somewhat at dawn and dusk. Coincidence range finders have also been adopted for the AMX 30 and the Pz. 61 while the Leopard has one capable of operating in either mode: normally it is to be used in the coincidence mode but it is expected that in each tank unit there will be at least a few gunners capable of using it in the stereoscopic mode in poor light, at dawn and dusk, when the coincidence mode is ineffective.

Optical range finders have not, however, found favour in Britain, nor have they appeared on Russian tanks up to and including the T-10 and the T-62. Only one British tank, the Conqueror, has had an optical range finder, of the split-image coincidence type, fitted across the commander's cupola. As a result, it had a shorter base and was, therefore, less accurate than the wide-base range finders fitted across other contemporary tanks, except the Japanese Type 61, which also has a short-base range finder fitted across the commander's cupola.

Instead of optical range finders, the up-gunned 105 mm Centurions and after them the Chieftain and the Vickers 37-ton tank have been provided with a ·5 in. ranging machine gun, which is used to fire short bursts of tracer bullets and, by observing the fall of the bullets, to obtain the range of the target. Compared with the optical range finder, the ranging machine gun is far less vulnerable to damage and calls for none of the skill and maintenance facilities which the former requires. It also takes into account such factors as the tilt of the tank or, more precisely, the cant of the gun trunnions, and the strength and direction of the wind, which the range finder does not. However, its range is limited and it cannot be used when range information is needed most, that is at long ranges, whereas the optical range finder can, even though its accuracy decreases with range.

In fact, the effectiveness of a ·5 in. machine gun stops short of 2,000 metres, while tank guns are expected to fire at up to 2,500 metres, or more and its adoption has been particularly incongruous in the case of the Chieftain whose 120 mm gun is obviously intended for fighting at long range. Moreover, when the ranging machine gun was tried in the prototypes of the Leopard, it was found that it resulted in a lower rate of engagement of successive targets than the optical range finder which was subsequently adopted in its place. Ranging with a machine gun also suffers from the disadvantage that it is not unobtrusive, and might give away the position of a tank prematurely.

During the early sixties a third type of range finder has made its appearance as a result of the development of lasers. It operates by sending out a single, very short pulse of laser radiation and provides a rapid, silent and very accurate means of ranging. In consequence, laser range finders have come to be regarded as the successors to both optical range finders and ranging machine guns and they have been installed in more than one experimental vehicle.

In the meantime an entirely different type of tank armament has appeared in the form of guided missiles. These dispense with the need for knowing the range since they do not follow a ballistic trajectory but are guided in flight. Being rockets, they also impose small, if any, forces on the vehicles from which they are launched and the size of their warheads, as well as their range, depends only on the size of their motors. They lend themselves well, therefore, to firing at distant targets and can be used relatively easily at ranges of 3,000 metres, or more, when it is increasingly difficult to achieve satisfactory results with guns.

How often tanks are likely to fight at such long ranges is another matter. Historical evidence, based on tank battles during the Second World War, points to most engagements taking place at less than 1,000 metres but the circumstances have changed since and there were cases, even then, of Russian IS tanks opening fire with their 122 mm guns at 2,000 metres. What is more telling, therefore, are the results of investigations carried out since 1945 into the ranges at which tanks are most likely to acquire their targets. The results vary, with the terrain, from just below 1,000 to about 1,500 metres, which does not preclude some engagements taking place at up to 3,000 metres but suggests that they are going to be very infrequent. Military requirements tend to go to extremes, however, instead of concentrating on the most likely conditions, and tanks are already expected to fight at up to 2,500 or even 3,000 metres. In view of this and the likelihood of demands for even longer ranges, as well as their own development, guided missiles are an increasingly attractive form of tank armament.

The development of surface-to-surface guided missiles with armour-piercing warheads started in Germany, in 1943, with an anti-tank rocket called the X-7, which was about to go into production when the war in Europe came to an end in 1945. After the war development of this type of missile was resumed in France, where it was first put into production in 1953 in the form of the SS-10. Since then many similar missiles with optical, line-of-sight command guidance and a trailing wire link for the transmission of signals have been developed and by 1966 the French Nord Aviation organisation, which has held the lead in this field, had produced more than 200,000 for the armed forces of 23 different countries.

In the meantime one of the Nord Aviation missiles, the SS-11, was mounted on the AMX 13 tank and this was followed, in the late fifties and early sixties by the installation of anti-tank guided missiles on British, Russian and French wheeled armoured vehicles, as well as that of the SS-11 in the German *Jagdpanzer* (*Rakete*). In all these cases, guided missiles provided a means of accurately delivering large warheads over long ranges with almost no weight penalty so far as the launch vehicles were concerned. The SS-11, for instance, has a 140 mm diameter shaped charge warhead, which is capable of penetrating 660 mm of armour, and a range of 3,000 metres (Pls. 82 and 83). However, in other respects the first generation missiles compare very unfavourably with tank guns. First, they have to be piloted all the way to the target, which calls for considerable skill and prolonged concentration on the part of the missile operators who are exposed at the same time to environmental disturbances. In consequence, the chances of scoring hits are likely to be much lower under battlefield conditions than at peacetime demonstrations. Second, the speeds of the first generation missiles are only of the order of 600 ft/sec, which means relatively long flight times and a low frequency of launching successive missiles. Moreover, they are also very bulky, an extreme being illustrated by the Australian-designed Malkara, which is 77 in long and has a span of 31 in (Pl. 84). In consequence, only a few rounds can be stored inside a vehicle and if the missiles are mounted outside, as the four SS-11 are on AMX 13, they are very vulnerable to damage.

The task of piloting the missile on to the target has been eased somewhat with the Vickers Vigilant, and the British Aircraft Corporation's Swingfire, by incorporating in them an auto-pilot (Pl. 85). However, a much bigger step forward was represented by the addition, in the early sixties, of an automatic guidance system to the SS-11 installation on the AMX 13. Its most important feature is that the position of the missile is monitored by an infra-red tracking instrument and fed by it to an electronic computer which guides the missile along the operator's line of sight. Thus the operator is relieved of the task of piloting the missile on to the target and needs only to keep the target in his sight. By the same token the missile is made very largely independent of the reflexes of its human controller, which bedevil the operation of the first-generation missiles.

Similar automatic guidance systems have been incorporated since in several second-generation missiles, which are typified by the Franco-German HOT, an acronym for *Haut subsonique*, *Optique*, *Télécommandé*. This has been developed by Nord-Aviation in collaboration with the Bölkow Company and, is launched from a tube, being much more compact than its predecessors. In fact, it is not much larger and no heavier than a round of 105 mm tank gun ammunition and as it is launched from a tube under automatic guidance it can be used to engage targets at short, as well as long, range. It is also faster than the first-generation missiles, having a cruising speed of 920 ft/sec.

Another second-generation missile is the Shillelagh, developed since 1959 in the United States by the Aeronutronic Division of the Ford Motor Company and adopted as the armament of the M551 Sheridan light tank. Instead of the trailing wire of the HOT, the Shillelagh has a micro-wave command link and it is launched from a 152 mm rifled gun, which can also fire conventional, medium-velocity unguided projectiles. This dual capability greatly increases the versatility of the Shillelagh-152 mm XM81 gun/launcher system, as it can engage tanks at long range with missiles and it can also engage targets much more economically at short range with ordinary projectiles. At the same time it can be accommodated in relatively light vehicles (Pls. 86 and 87).

The Shillelagh—gun/launcher system is clearly an attractive alternative to high velocity tank guns but it also has its disadvantages. First, the Shillelagh still requires its controller to keep the target in his sight for several seconds and to this extent it is still dependent on human reflexes. Secondly, the missile control system is inevitably complex and even if the reliability of the components is very high their sheer number increases the chances of malfunctioning. Third, both the Shillelagh and the 152 mm medium-velocity projectile must rely on shaped charge warheads for their armour-piercing performance. In consequence, if this form of armament were adopted for battle tanks it would free opposing tanks from the threat of attack by high velocity armour-piercing shot and make it possible for them to acquire a higher degree of immunity, since protection against attack only with shaped charge warheads is easier to devise than protection against both forms of attack.

The answer to this problem lies in developing gun/missile launcher systems to fire APDS projectiles in addition to others. A price would have to be paid for this in increases in recoil loads and an equally undesirable increase in the variety of the tank ammunition, which complicates the task of the tank crews in battle. As it is, tanks require at least one other type of round in addition to their armour piercing rounds. In most cases this has taken the form of a conventional high-explosive round whose artillery-type shell is fired with a muzzle velocity of 2,400 to 2,600 ft/sec. An alternative to this is the high-explosive, squash-head, or HESH, projectile which was originally developed in Britain for destroying concrete fortifications but which has taken the place of HE shells in British tank gun ammunition from the 120 gun of the Conqueror onwards. It has also been adopted, together with the British 105 mm gun, in the U.S. M60, where it is known as the HEP, or "high-explosive, plastic", and in the German Leopard.

The principal feature of the HESH projectile is that it has a soft, thin-walled nose which is squashed on impact so that its charge explodes in close contact with the surface of the target. It lacks the fragmentation effect of a conventional HE shell but it produces at least as much blast and is much more effective against armour, as well as concrete. In fact, in Britain it was considered superior to HEAT projectiles and was even considered, during the fifties, as a possible replacement for all other armour-defeating projectiles but it has been accepted since primarily as an HE projectile. The effect it has against armour is due to the explosion of its charge in close contact with the surface of the armour which generates stress waves in it and, if it is large enough in relation to the thickness of the armour, the intensity of the stress waves is such that they cause fracture of the inside surface of the armour followed by the throwing off of lethal metal scabs. By the same token, HESH projectiles can be made ineffective by spaced or sandwich armour which prevents the generation of sufficiently intense stress waves in the inner plate and rules out the possibility of using them as the primary armour-defeating ammunition.

A dual, high explosive and armour-piercing capability can also be achieved with HEAT projectiles if they are large enough and the shell fired from the 152 mm XM81 gun/launcher is, in fact, of such a "general-purpose high-explosive anti-tank" type. This suggests the possibility of a single type of ammunition, which would greatly simplify the operation of tanks as well as their design. Unfortunately, any "general-purpose" projectile represents a compromise and is bound to be inferior in any one role to a projectile developed specifically for it.

What is more likely is further diversification in tank weapons, to bridge the gap between the increasingly powerful main armament and the rifle-calibre machine guns. Since the middle of the Second World War U.S. tanks have, in fact, been carrying ·5 in, as well as ·3 in, machine guns, but these are more powerful than necessary for the anti-personnel role of the rifle-calibre machine-guns and not powerful enough for most other purposes. The smallest inermediate weapon worth having is a 20 mm automatic cannon, which can be used against light armoured vehicles, as well as other, "soft" targets, and so lead to economies in the use of the main armament. A gun of this calibre, a 20 mm Polsten, was mounted in place of the usual "co-axial" machine gun in the first few Centurion I prototypes. But the first tank to be produced with it was the Swiss Pz.61, which has a 20 mm Oerlikon gun mounted alongside its 105 mm gun, instead of a rifle-calibre machine-gun, which is mounted externally, on top of the turret. A similar arrangement of weapons has been adopted on the AMX 30 where the 20 mm gun can be elevated independently of the 105 mm gun for use against helicopters, which enhances still further the effectiveness of the tank weapon system.

CHAPTER 4

Design of Turrets and Hulls

FOR all the changes which have taken place in tank armament, the general layout of tanks remains much the same as that introduced in 1918 by the Renault F.T. light tank. In other words, almost all tanks continue to have a driving compartment at the front, a fighting compartment surmounted by a rotating turret mounting the main armament in the middle and an engine compartment at the rear (Fig. III).

There have been several changes, however, within the classic layout. One is the elimination of the hull machine gunner, who sat beside the driver in almost all tanks in service in 1945. The mounting of a rifle-calibre machine gun in the front of the hull in addition to the customary "co-axial" machine gun mounted with the gun in the turret was a custom which grew out of the mistaken belief in the value of a multiplicity of machine guns—a belief responsible at one time for tanks having as many as seven or even eight machine guns and a good deal of effort wasted on the development of multi-turreted vehicles. By 1945 it became obvious, however, that the 45, or so, cubic feet occupied by the hull machine gunner were quite out of proportion to the value of the weapon he operated and so both were eliminated. As a result, the size of tank crews was reduced from five to four men—driver, gunner, loader and commander.

The move to four man crews was led by the Russian IS 1 of 1943, followed by the British Centurion and the Russian T-44. The last to have a hull machine gunner was the U.S. M47, which inherited the hull of the much earlier M26 tank. But there has been at least one more tank with a five-man crew, the U.S. M103, in which there is an assistant loader in the turret to help handle the heavy 120 mm ammunition. All other tanks built since 1945, have had a crew of no more than four men, which is generally regarded as necessary and sufficient to operate the conventional type of battle tank.

Of the four, the gunner and the commander are invariably located behind each other in the turret on one side of the gun while the loader is located on the other side. The loader's position is generally on the left of the gun although in Russian tanks, as in the German Panther and Tiger, it has been on the right. In either case, he needs room to handle rounds which may be 36 in long and if he is to do this without undue effort he must be able to stand upright, which sets a limit of about 5 ft 6 in to the minimum height from the hull floor to the turret roof—assuming that only short men are selected for loaders. The same height is arrived at by adding the minimum height of the hull necessary to accommodate a seated driver, which is about 3 ft 4 in, and the height which the turret needs to have not only to accommodate the gun but also to allow it to be loaded when it is depressed a few degrees. Given a moderate ground clearance of 18 in, this leads to a height of at least 7 ft 0 in from the ground to the top of the turret roof. Tanks are generally higher than this, however. The additional height is due mainly to the requirement that guns have a depression of as much as 10 degrees below the horizontal, so that tanks can fire from reverse slopes instead of having to come up on to the crests of ground waves and exposing themselves much more. Unfortunately, the greater the depression of the gun the greater also is the amount of room required within the turret for the corresponding upward movement of the breech. In consequence, in some tanks, such as the Russian T54, depression has been limited to 5 degrees to keep their overall height to a minimum, in order to reduce the target they offer in the open.

The gun and its ammunition also govern the minimum width of a conventional tank, since the diameter of the turret ring must be sufficiently large for the breech to swing down when the muzzle is elevated and for the guns to be loaded in this, as well as intermediate positions. In consequence, as the size of the guns increased so did the turret ring diameter, from 69 in in the U.S. M4, through 74 in in the Centurions to 85 in in the U.S. M48 and M60. In most cases, so far, the width of tanks has been considerably greater than their turret ring diameter but as gun size increases the additional width needs to be reduced to a minimum by bringing the turret ring out, over the tracks, close to the overall width of the tank, which is restricted by the dimensions of railways, bridges, tunnels and other installations. In particular, the Berne International Railway Gauge prescribes a maximum width of 10 ft 4 in for loads carried by rail and any tank wider than this cannot be freely transported by railways in many parts of the world.

Attempts have been made to circumvent the limitations of the classic layout by modifying it but this has met with limited success. One of the

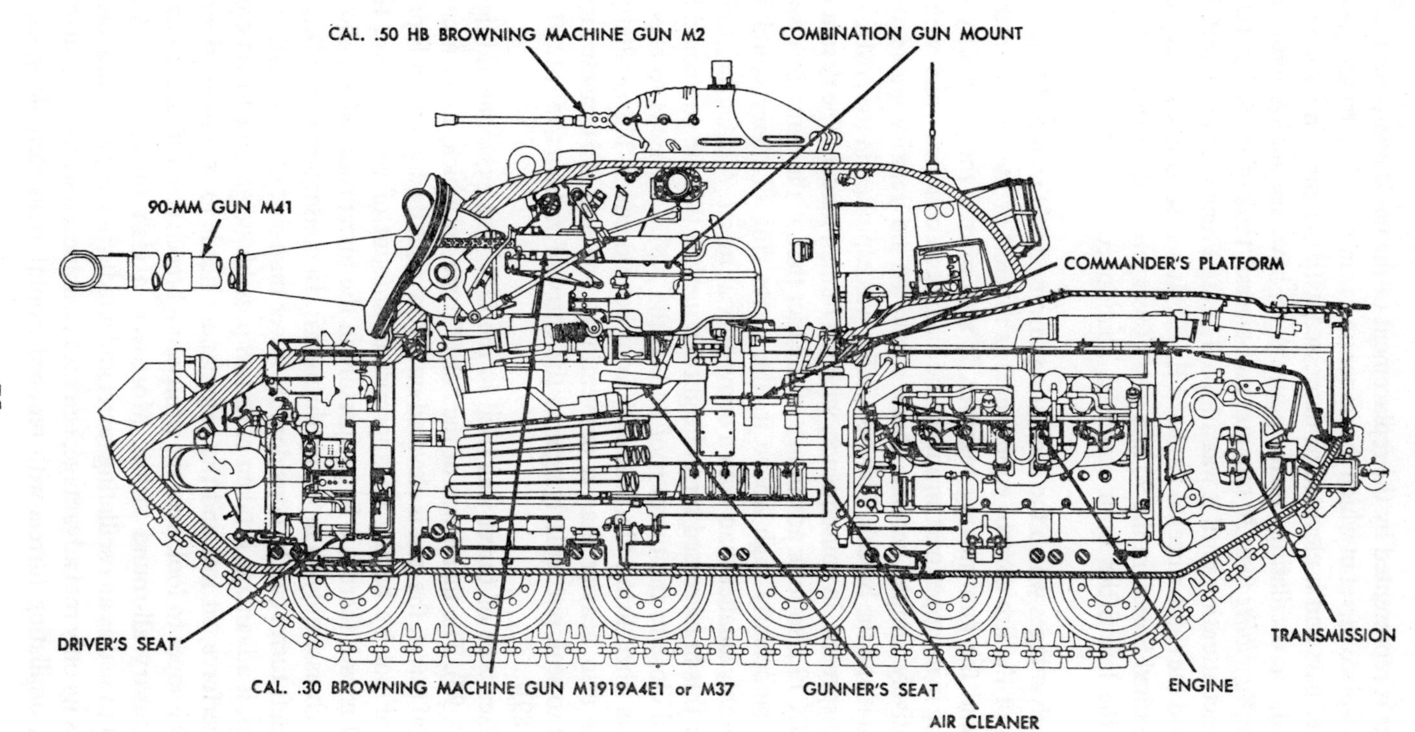

Fig. III Cross section of the United States M48A2 medium tank.

attempts is represented by the replacement of the usual one-piece turret by a two-piece turret in which the upper part is mounted on trunnions in the lower part and is elevated or depressed with the gun. The trunnion-mounted, or oscillating, turret appears to have originated with the German *Kugelblitz* twin 30 mm gun anti-aircraft tank of 1944, but it did not attract attention until it was adopted in the French AMX 50 and 13 tanks and the eight-wheeled Panhard E.B.R. It was subsequently copied in the United States, in the 90 mm gun T69 experimental medium tank, but in the late fifties both countries abandoned its development for tanks.

The advantages which the oscillating turret offered included a simplification of the fire control equipment, as a result of the optical instruments and the gun moving together. It also offered the possibility of installing in its upper part an automatic loading mechanism which would be relatively simple because there would be no relative movement between it and the breech. This possibility was exploited in the AMX 13, which dispensed, in consequence, with the human loader. The design of the AMX 13 also took advantage of the fact that, if the trunnions were located sufficiently high above it, the turret ring diameter could be considerably smaller than with a conventional turret. A price had to be paid for this in increased turret height but against this the gun could be mounted close to the turret roof and so the AMX 13 needs to expose itself less when firing "hull down" from behind cover. The oscillating turret is also heavier than a conventional one and it is much more difficult to seal, particularly against the entry of radioactive dust (Pls. 88 and 89).

Another type of turret was tried in the U.S. T92 experimental light tank (Pl. 90). The turret was of the "cleft" type, in which, as in a conventional turret, the gun is elevated on its own but its depression is provided for not by having an appropriate amount of room within the turret. Instead, there is a large aperture in the turret roof, which allows the breech assembly to move up through it. In consequence, the height of the cleft turret can be considerably lower than that of a conventional one. But, if advantage is taken of its low possible height, the turret crew must, perforce, sit low and the commander needs to be provided with long periscopes to look over the protruding breech cover if he is to have the necessary all-round vision. Moreover, a cleft turret is about as difficult to seal as an oscillating turret and a reduction in the frontal area, which is its only real advantage, can also be achieved with other turrets. In fact, oscillating turrets with reduced frontal areas were designed at about the same time as the cleft turret of the T92 and a conventional turret with a reduced frontal area has since been developed for the M60A1E1 tank (Pl. 91).

In contrast to the T92, which had two men in its turret, the M60A1E1 has the usual three, with the gunner and loader sitting low on either side of the 152 mm gun/launcher and the commander sitting high directly behind the gun. As a result, the turret of the M60A1E1 has a relatively narrow frontal area and the commander has the necessary all-round vision but he can only be positioned directly behind the gun, as he was already in tanks such as the Pz. Kpfw. IV, when the diameter of the turret ring is large in relation to the inboard length of the gun and the length of rounds.

Yet another turret development has been the installation on the U.S. M48 and M60 tanks of a machine gun cupola on top of the main turret (Pl. 92). The machine gun cupola is a refinement of the long standing practice of providing tank commanders with an externally mounted machine gun and it represents a combination of the latter with the commander's observation cupola. It is, however, much larger than well-designed observation cupolas, particularly as it mounts an unnecessarily large, ·5 in machine gun, and it brings about a most unfortunate enlargement in the silhouette of the M48 and M60 tanks. It also makes tank commanders more vulnerable as it raises their heads above the level of the main turret armour. In the light of all this the remotely controlled rifle-calibre machine guns mounted on top of the observation cupolas of the Chieftain and the AMX 30 are more sensible, especially as the only real justification of machine guns mounted on tops of turrets is close-in defence. But all auxiliary machine guns operated by tank commanders are open to the basic objection that they divert the commanders' attention from their primary command functions and reduce them, for some time at least, to the role of machine gunners. If machine guns are to be mounted on tops of turrets, there is much to be said, therefore, for the alternative arrangement whereby loaders are responsible for them, as they have been in Russian tanks and continue to be in the Swiss Pz. 61.

Somewhat different objections apply to the possible combination of the duties of the commander and the gunner and the consequent reduction of the turret crew to two men. As it is, the commander normally identifies or selects targets and is commonly provided with overriding gun controls, so that he can dispense with the gunner. But there is always the danger that, if the functions are combined, the commander/gunner will become preoccupied with gunnery, or rocketry, and lose grasp of the overall tactical situation. The consequences of this happening would be particularly serious where the commander not only commands his own tank but also a platoon, or troop, of three to five tanks. In fact, the case is not so much against combining the duties of tank commanders and gunners as for having some tanks from which unit commanders can exercise effective tactical leadership and in which, therefore, they are free of tasks connected with the tanks' immediate operation. A conclusion could be drawn from this that there should be special commanders' tanks but these would greatly complicate the operation of tank units and increase the vulnerability of unit commanders by drawing enemy fire. Special commanders' tanks are therefore unacceptable on tactical, as well as economic, grounds and every tank has to meet the needs of unit commanders.

Turret design is also affected by the driver. In particular, if the height of the driving compartment is reduced the position of the gun trunnions can be lowered in relation to the ground and the overall height of the tank can be reduced without reducing the depression of its gun. But to achieve a significant reduction in height it is necessary to abandon the conventional driving position and to have the driver adopt a prone or supine attitude. In either case, the height of the hull can be lowered to about 2 ft 9 in but the supine position is generally superior and has been adopted in the Chieftain.

The alternative to reducing the height of the driving compartment is to bring the driver into the turret. This implies, however, not only a larger turret but also a complicated counter-rotating sub-turret within the main turret or bringing the turret round to a fixed position, in which the driver faces forward, every time the vehicle is about to move. The latter is feasible in the case of self-propelled guns, which are not expected to change their firing positions as frequently and rapidly as tanks, and the second solution has, in fact, been adopted in a series of self-propelled guns developed during the late forties and early fifties in the United States. They include the M52 (T98) 105 mm and T99 155 mm s.p. howitzers, the M53 (T97) 155 mm s.p. gun and the M55 (T108) 203 mm s.p. howitzer. The Swedish VEAK 40 experimental self-propelled anti-aircraft gun also has its driver in the turret but in more recent U.S. self-propelled guns the driver is located, once again, in the hull.

The converse of bringing the driver into the turret is much more attractive. It amounts to abandoning the rotating turret and mounting the main armament in the hull. This results in turretless vehicles, which have none of the width problems associated with turret rings and which are potentially lower than others. They are not much lower, however, than their turreted counterparts when they have to accommodate large guns which are elevated and depressed in relation to the hull between the usual limits of +20 to −10 degrees. Moreover, the guns can only be provided with limited arcs of traverse and even this requires a considerable amount of additional room in the fighting compartments, as well as preventing turretless vehicles from engaging targets on the move, unless they happen to be to their immediate front. In consequence, after enjoying a spell of popularity with the German and Soviet Armies during the Second World War, turretless vehicles gradually declined in importance. The only recent examples of the original type of turretless vehicle which are of any consequence are the Russian ASU-85 and the German *Jagdpanzer* (*Kanone*) and both of these are limited-purpose anti-tank vehicles.

A very different and much more advanced type of turretless vehicle is represented by the S-tank developed in Sweden since 1956. In it the gun mounting is fixed in relation to the hull and the gun is elevated or depressed by altering the pitch of the hull, by means of an adjustable hydro-pneumatic suspension, and traversed by turning the whole vehicle. In consequence, there is no need in it for the space required in earlier turretless vehicles by the movement of the breech end of the gun, so that its height can be kept low and the gun can be mounted close to the roof of the fighting compartment, as in an oscillating turret (Pl. 93). The adoption of a fixed gun mounting and the consequent elimination of movement between the gun and the ammunition magazine has also made it possible to install a relatively simple—and therefore reliable—automatic loading mechanism. A human loader could then be dispensed with, which has saved a considerable amount of space within the tank, making it more compact still. What is more, the addition of an automatic loading mechanism to a gun fixed in the vehicle has made it possible to develop an integrated set of driving and gun controls. These are provided not only for the driver/gunner, who sits on one side of the gun, but also for the commander, who sits on the other side. The commander can, therefore, take over control of the tank and when speed is important he can engage targets more quickly by himself, instead of acting through other men.

The S-tank also possesses an advantage in having a set of controls for driving in reverse, which are operated by the third crewman who sits behind the driver, facing backwards, and who also operates the tank's radio sets. The provision for driving backwards as easily as forwards is peculiar to the S-tank and enables it to withdraw not only pointing its gun in the direction of the enemy but, at the same time, presenting its least vulnerable side to him. The S-tank differs from other battle tanks in yet another respect, namely in having its engine compartment at the front. This has reduced the overhang of its gun barrel, as well as providing the crew with additional protection against frontal attack, and is only found elsewhere in light vehicles, such as the AMX 13 and the T92, where the engine is small enough to be located alongside the driver and its forward location leads to more compact layouts.

What the S-tank does not possess is the ability to fire its main armament on the move, as turreted vehicles can, unless the target happens to be directly in front of it. But even turreted vehicles have to stop to fire accurately and the S-tank can do this at least as quickly as they can, due to its simplified firing procedure.

Attempts at making tanks fire accurately on the move amount to the stabilisation of guns against angular motions of vehicles by reference to gyroscopes mounted on the gun cradles. Stabilised power controls were already applied to the elevation of the 75 mm guns of the U.S. M4 medium tanks but their utility proved extremely limited and they have not been fitted on tanks produced in the United States since 1945. In contrast, stabilised power controls have been applied since then not only to the elevation of the guns but also to the traverse of the turrets of all the Centurions from the Mark 2 onwards. A similar system, which holds the gun in space on a fixed bearing and angle of elevation on the basis of signals from two rate gyroscopes, has also been installed in the Chieftain and Russian T-54 tanks also have guns stabilised in elevation.

Other developments in tank weapon systems include automatic ejection of spent cartridge cases, which is a concomitant of automatic loading mechanisms installed in the AMX 13 and the S-tank and which puts an end to the nuisance of spent cases, emitting heat and noxious fumes in the fighting compartment. Similar results are obtained with combustible cartridge cases, which have been introduced with the 152 mm general-purpose rounds of the M551 Sheridan, and the bag charges of the Chieftain, although they all require a more complicated breech mechanism than the usual sliding block type. Propellant charges contained in combustible cartridge cases and bag charges also offer a considerable saving in weight over charges contained in conventional brass cartridge cases and are less likely to catch fire if hit by hot metallic fragments when tank armour has been perforated. The risk of propellant fires has been reduced still further in the Chieftain by locating its bag charges in water-jacketed containers.

Guns themselves have been fitted with fume extractors or bore evacuators, and thermal shielding. The fume extractor first appeared on the U.S. M46 and consists of an annular chamber around the barrel which is connected to the bore by suitably shaped ports. The ports allow pressure to build up in the chamber as the projectile passes them and the subsequent discharge from the chamber causes a flow of bore fumes towards the muzzle, which helps to minimise the release of gases into the fighting compartment. Thermal shielding first appeared on the Centurions and reduces the bending of gun barrels due to non-uniform cooling by wind or rain, or heating by solar radiation.

Guns have also been fitted with muzzle brakes, which reduce recoil forces by deflecting propellant gases as they flow out of the muzzle and allow, therefore, larger guns to be fitted in tanks in relation to their weight. In the case of conventional, turreted vehicles the recoil force exerted by the gun cannot be much more than one and a half times the weight of the vehicle, for it to be stable. This condition has been met, however, in most recently built tanks without resorting to muzzle brakes because they are heavier than they need to be as gun platforms.

The additional weight is due to their armour. How much heavier they are varies according to the importance attached to armour protection. One extreme is represented by the view, which has prevailed in Britain, that heavy armour is worth having, particularly when it comes to tank versus tank duels. In consequence, the Chieftain is heavily armoured and heavier than all other contemporary tanks. The other extreme is represented by the conclusion reached in France that relatively thin armour is all that is necessary, since the difference between it and the thickest possible armour cannot make much difference to the overall probability of survival on the battlefield. As a result the AMX 30 is lighter than all its contemporaries and enjoys all the attendant advantages.

The actual thickness of armour has not advanced much on the maxima arrived at by the end of the Second World War. For instance, Tiger II already had a frontal hull plate 150 mm thick, inclined at 50 degrees to the vertical, and this is still indicative of the maximum protection likely to be had by heavy tanks. Similarly, the protection of several medium tanks is not very different from that afforded by the frontal plate of the Panther, which was 80 mm thick and inclined at 55 degrees to the vertical. The armour is, however, being used much more effectively, both by sloping it and by redistributing it over the frontal arc at the expense of protection elsewhere, in keeping with statistical studies of the most likely directions of attack.

Sloping of armour is particularly effective against AP projectiles and so far as horizontal attack is concerned plates inclined at 50 to 60 degrees to the vertical are equivalent to vertical plates of much greater thickness than their own thickness in the horizontal direction, as shown in Fig. IV. Were it not so there would be little point in inclining the plates for while the horizontal thickness of the plate increases with the angle of inclination so does its length for a given height of the area to be protected, with the result that the weights of vertical and sloped plates of the same horizontal thickness are the same. In fact, sloped plates are much more effective on a weight basis than vertical plates. For instance, a plate 100 mm thick inclined at 60 degrees to the vertical has a horizontal thickness of 200 mm but, so far as ballistic protection is concerned, it is equivalent to a vertical plate some 300 mm thick. The exact effect of sloping of armour depends on the projectile, sloped plates being more effective in the case of the APDS shot than in that of full bore projectiles with caps, or with blunt noses which have been used with Russian tank guns.

On the other hand, sloped plates are not very different, on a weight basis, from vertical plates when it comes to shaped charge projectiles, or missiles. In this case the most effective form of protection is obtained by having a detonating screen in front of the main plate, to set off the shaped charge at the greatest possible stand-off distance. Mild steel skirting plates were introduced for this purpose in 1943 on the German Pz. Kpfw. IV and skirting plates have also been fitted since to the Centurion, Conqueror and Chieftain but while they might be effective against the smaller infantry anti-tank weapons much greater stand-off distances than those provided by the skirting plates are needed against large shaped-charge warheads. In contrast, even narrowly spaced armour is very effective against squash head projectiles. Spaced armour has also been effective against APDS shots but in general it has not been as effective against the different types of AP projectiles as one-piece armour of the same total thickness and the design of the armour envelope has been almost entirely dictated by this form of attack.

Attack by AP projectiles has also governed the choice of material, for armour, which is nickel-chrome-molybdenum steel, most frequently in the form of homogeneous, machinable quality rolled plate having an

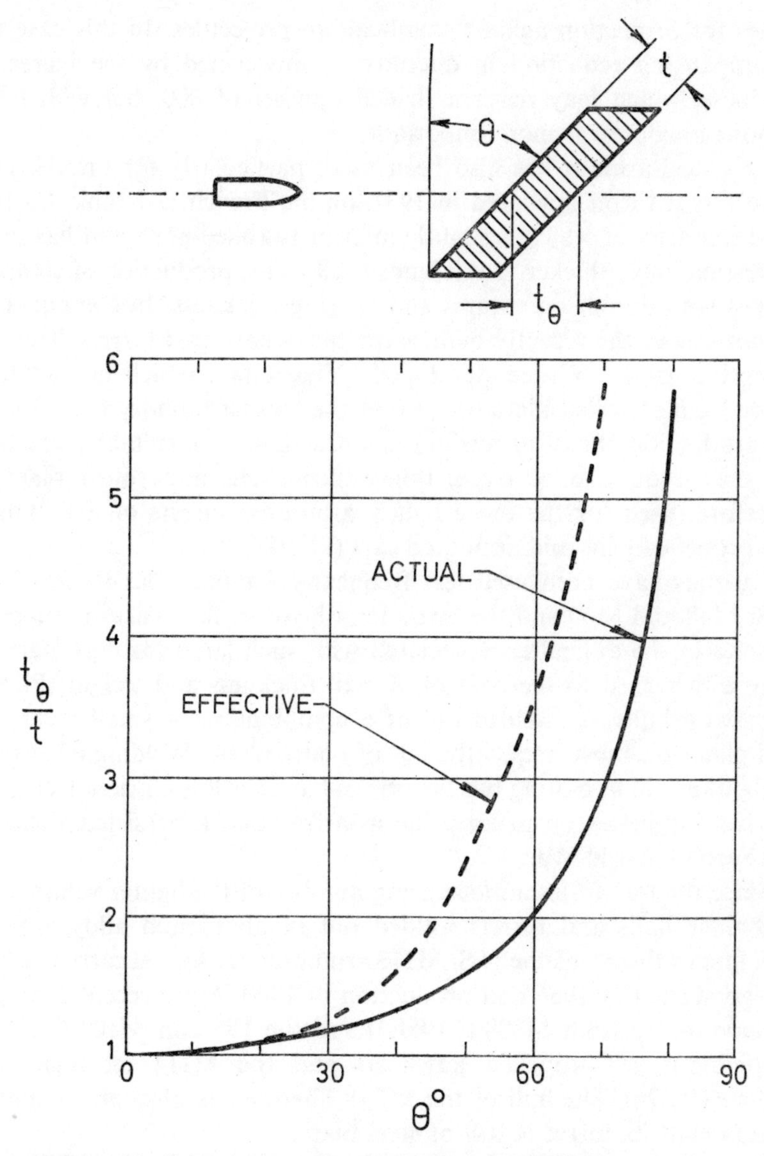

Fig. IV Effect of inclining armour plate on its horizontal thickness.

ultimate tensile strength of 140,000 to 160,000 lb/in^2 and a Brinell hardness number of about 300. This has best met the twin requirements of toughness to absorb the energy of heavy, high velocity projectiles without cracking and of hardness to resist their penetration. Hard and face-hardened armour has also been used but only in the form of thin plates for protection against small-calibre projectiles. In this case the accompanying reduction in ductility is outweighed by the increased hardness, which may reach a Brinell number of 600, but with thick armour toughness is more important.

Cast steel armour has also been used, particularly for turrets, ever since a cast turret appeared in 1931, on the French D-1 tank. Casting produces armour which is slightly inferior to rolled plate and has to be correspondingly thicker. But it lends itself to the production of complex shapes with double curvatures and varying thickness. In consequence, all but one of the recently built battle tanks have cast turrets. The one exception is the Vickers-developed "Vijayanta", which has a turret welded out of rolled plate because of the lack of foundry facilities for the production of cast turrets in India. Casting is not suitable, however, for the production of large, thin-walled shells and rolled plate is, therefore, used for the more lightly armoured turrets of light tanks, self-propelled guns and armoured cars (Pl. 94).

Castings have been used less frequently for hulls but those of the U.S. M48 and M60 and the Swiss Pz. 61 are, in fact, cast in one piece in spite of the difficulties associated with such large castings, particularly with regard to the control of wall thickness and weight (Pl. 95). Otherwise hulls are welded out of a combination of smaller castings and plates or, most frequently, out of plates alone. Welding of armour is about as old as casting but the original and far less efficient technique of rivetting plates on to an angle iron framework persisted well into the Second World War.

Since the mid-fifties an increasing number of the lighter vehicles has had their hulls and turrets welded out of aluminium alloy armour. The first of these was the U.S. M113 armoured personnel carrier, whose design started in 1956 and production in 1960. More recent examples include the 105 mm M108 (T195E1) and the 155 mm M109 (T196E1) amphibious self-propelled howitzers and the M114 reconnaissance vehicle (Pl. 96). The hull of the M551 Sheridan is also of aluminium armour but its turret is still of steel plate.

The M113 was designed and produced by the Ordnance Division of the Food Machinery and Chemical Corporation and its hull is welded out of Kaiser aluminium alloy 5083, an aluminium-magnesium alloy with an ultimate tensile strength of 46,000 lb/in^2. To achieve the same degree of ballistic protection as steel armour this type of alloy has to be about three times as thick and its density is 0·096 lb/in^3, compared with 0·283 lb/in^3 for steel. In consequence, its areal density, that is the weight per unit of surface area, is about the same as that of ballistically equivalent steel armour.

The use of aluminium armour has not, therefore, produced any major weight savings over steel armour. The relative position of the two materials is well brought out by comparing the original, experimental version of the M113 carrier, the T113, with its steel-hulled alternative, the T117. Under comparable conditions the two vehicles weighed 14,529 and 15,951 lb respectively, so that, after deducting 366 lb from the latter because of differences in engine installations, the actual weight difference amounted to 956 lb, or a 6 per cent saving on the weight of the steel version. What weight savings there are come from the increased rigidity of aluminium hulls due to the inevitably greater thickness of their walls, which makes it possible to reduce the weight of purely structural components.

Other non-ferrous metals have also been investigated, the most promising being titanium alloys. These have ultimate tensile strengths and ductility comparable with steel alloys and yet have a density of only 0·16 lb/in^3. Unfortunately, titanium alloys are also much more difficult to process and very much more expensive, in contrast to aluminium alloys.

Non-metallic armour has also been developed, particularly for very light-weight protection. In its original form it consisted of polyester resin bonded glass-fibre laminates, such as Doron, which has been used in the form of small plates in armour vests. However, the areal density of this type of plastic armour is virtually the same as that of steel armour of the same ballistic merit and it offers no advantage even for very lightly armoured vehicles. More promising results have been obtained with composite armour consisting of an outer layer of a ceramic material, such as aluminium oxide, backed by resin bonded glass-fibres. Composites of this kind represent an attempt to exploit the hardness of ceramic materials and, at the same time, to overcome their brittleness but they have not been effective against more than one hit. The lightest type of armour is represented by layers of nylon cloth. This too has been used chiefly for protective vests but blanket-type nylon armour has been tried on the U.S. M107 (T235) 175 mm self-propelled gun as a form of very light, demountable protection against shell fragments (Pl. 97).

Polymeric materials can also be used for radiological protection. They cannot provide shielding against the high-intensity, high-energy radiation from nuclear explosions but some of them are effective where lower intensities and energies are involved. For instance, in low flux environments polyethylene provides effective shielding against neutrons because of its high percentage of hydrogen atoms and its effectiveness is greatly increased by the addition of a relatively small quantity of a boron filler. Thus, borated polyethylene can be used to provide additional light-weight shielding in the form of liners for turrets and hulls and polyethylene liners can also help to reduce the effects of shaped charge penetrations.

CHAPTER 5

Automotive Components

ONE of the consequences of the relatively heavy weight of tanks is that they need powerful engines. But, since tanks vary in size, the need is generally considered not in terms of the required engine output but in terms of horse-power per ton, which governs much of the actual or potential performance of tanks as automotive vehicles, whatever their size.

In particular, the amount of horse-power which a tank has per ton sets a limit to the maximum speed it can attain. On level road surfaces the maximum attainable speed is, in fact, directly proportional to the horse-power per ton since the resistance to the motion of tanks is an almost constant fraction of their weight. The actual magnitude of the resistance to motion is such that 0·2 to 0·3 net horse-power per ton is required per mile per hour. However, the gross horse-power per ton, which is generally quoted, needs to be considerably higher than this, since 30 to 40 per cent of it is lost in driving the cooling fans, in the transmission and elsewhere, and the actual maximum road speed depends also on the overall transmission ratio.

The horse-power per ton also governs the acceleration of a tank, which is particularly important because of its influence on the speed of changing firing positions. Likewise, it governs the speed with which the tank can climb gradients and the average speed of travel in varied terrain, which is directly proportional to horse-power per ton.

There are good reasons, therefore, for having as much horse-power per ton as possible. There are various limits, however, to the amount of power which tanks can effectively use and no more than about 20 gross b.h.p. per ton has usually been aimed at. But even this, in the case of a typical 40-ton tank, means an engine of 800 b.h.p. and automotive engines of this size are generally not available, least of all in a form suitable for tanks where space is at a premium. Therefore, engines have to be specially built for tanks and they need to have a high specific output.

The approach towards greater specific output adopted after the Second World War in Britain, France and the United States centred mainly on the application of fuel injection to spark ignition engines. In 1945 all tank engines of this type used carburetters but in Germany work was going already on a fuel injection version of the Maybach HL 230 23-litre V-12 used in the Panther and Tiger II, which was to produce 900, instead of 700, b.h.p. at 3,000 r.p.m. Work on this type of engine was continued after the war in France, where it led to the construction of a 1,000 b.h.p. fuel injection engine for the AMX 50. At about the same time fuel injection was applied in Britain to the Rolls-Royce Meteor 27-litre V-12. The Meteor with fuel injection, which was produced by Rover Ltd. and installed in the Conqueror, developed 810 b.h.p. at 2,800 r.p.m., compared with 635 b.h.p. at 2,550 r.p.m. of the carburetted version which continued to be used in the Centurion.

The S.U. fuel injection system adopted for the Meteor was subsequently also adopted by the U.S. Army for the 29·4-litre AVI-1790-8 V-12 engine of the M48A2 tank, whose production started in 1956. In this case, however, fuel injection was adopted in an attempt to improve the specific fuel consumption of the engine, whose original carburetter version suffered from poor distribution, as much as to improve its output. Indeed, only a very modest increase in output was obtained, the AVI-1790-8 giving 865 b.h.p. compared with 821 b.h.p. of the earlier, carburetted AV-1790-5, both at 2,800 r.p.m.

The AV-1790 engines are the largest of a rationalised series of engines developed by the Continental Aviation and Engineering Corporation for the U.S. Army. The series consists of air-cooled engines based on a common cylinder size and it represented a major post-war development programme of the U.S. Army Ordnance, its first result being the installation of the AV-1790-5 in the M46 tank. The adoption of air-cooling stemmed from the earlier use in American tanks of air-cooled radial aircraft engines and had the merit of eliminating the vulnerable radiators and plumbing associated with liquid cooling. But it also meant the acceptance of a somewhat lower specific output, since direct cooling by air is not as effective as liquid cooling at carrying heat away from the hottest parts of engines. In addition to being air-cooled, the Ordnance-Continental engines were also peculiar in including among the smaller models some with mechanically driven superchargers. An example of this is the 6-cylinder horizontally opposed AOS-895-3 used in the M41 tank, an engine which has a swept volume of 14·7 litres and produces 500 b.h.p. at 2,800 r.p.m.

But, for all this, the development of spark ignition tank engines was overtaken during the mid-fifties by policy changes in favour of diesels. The change arose out of a somewhat belated realisation of the great importance of fuel economy in the operation of tanks and in both Britain and the United States it meant a reversal of the decisions taken during the Second World War to concentrate on spark ignition engines. The Soviet Army, on the other hand, had consistently used diesel engines in all its medium and heavy armoured vehicles built since 1939. In fact, it used one type of engine, the V-2, a water-cooled, 38·9-litre V-12 rated at up to 550 b.h.p. at 2,150 r.p.m.

The change to diesels manifested itself in the United States in the adoption of the AVDS-1790 compression ignition engine for the M60 tank. The AVDS-1790 is, in effect, a diesel conversion of the earlier AV-1790 spark ignition engine and, fitted with two exhaust driven superchargers, it has a gross output of 750 b.h.p. at 2,400 r.p.m. This is evidently less than the 825 b.h.p. of the AV-1790-5 but the net horsepower is, in fact, slightly higher, being 630 compared with 625. The net gain is due to the use of exhaust driven turbochargers, which eliminated the need for silencers and the losses arising from this source, and by the lower heat rejection of a compression ignition engine, which has reduced the required cooling fan power.

In Britain the revival of interest in diesels was heralded by the appearance of a 24-litre V-8 Rover engine designed during the early fifties. However, there was a spark ignition, as well as a compression ignition, version of that engine and it was only around 1956 that decisions were clearly taken in favour of diesels. At the time experience with a Rootes opposed-piston two-stroke truck diesel suggested that this type of engine was particularly suitable for operation on gasoline as well as diesel oil and this led to a family of so-called "multi-fuel" engines developed by the Fighting Vehicles Research and Development Establishment in conjunction with Leyland Motors Ltd., and Rolls-Royce Ltd. The largest of them is the Leyland L.60, which was developed for the Chieftain and was subsequently adopted also for the Vickers 37-ton tank. This 19-litre engine is rated in the Chieftain at 700 b.h.p., at a crankshaft speed of 2,400 r.p.m., and is essentially a modernised version of the Junkers 6-cylinder opposed-piston two-stroke aircraft diesel of the thirties. As such, it has the advantage of an inherently low specific fuel consumption combined with a relatively high specific output and the disadvantage of highly stressed pistons, whose hot crowns were, nevertheless, thought to be essential for operation on a wide range of fuels.

However, opposed pistons were not found to be necessary in other "multi-fuel" tank engines developed in Germany and France. These too are diesels, modified to make them better able to operate, in an emergency, on lower cetane fuels, down to the medium grade gasoline commonly specified for military spark ignition engines. In fact, all the "multi-fuel" engines are diesels and their development has been attended by a good deal of unnecessary fuss but it has brought about a considerable improvement in fuel economy on the earlier, spark ignition tank engines.

The German "multi-fuel" engines are diesels with pre-combustion chambers and they form another rationalised series based on a common cylinder size. They have been developed by Daimler-Benz AG since the early fifties and their first application to tanks was in the Swiss Pz. 58. The engine installed in this tank and the more recent Pz. 61 is a 29·9-litre V-8 which develops 630 b.h.p. at 2,200 r.p.m. A similar, MB 837 Aa engine, developing 500 b.h.p., powers the German *Jagdpanzer* but a larger engine has been developed for the Leopard. This is the MB 838 Ca, a 37·4-litre V-10, which develops 830 b.h.p. at 2,200 r.p.m. and not only has two more cylinders than the MB 837 Aa but also a gear-driven centrifugal supercharger for each bank of five cylinders.

In France prototypes of the AMX 30 built in 1960 were still powered by a spark ignition engine, the S.O.F.A.M. GSds, a 12-cylinder horizontally opposed model developing 720 b.h.p. The production versions of the AMX 30 are, however, powered by a diesel designed by the Hispano Suiza Company, the HS 110, which is also of the 12-cylinder horizontally opposed type and produces 720 b.h.p.

Yet another type of diesel engine was built by the Mitsubishi Nippon Heavy Industries Ltd. when the development of tanks was resumed during the early fifties in Japan. The engine, model 12HM, is a 29·6-litre V-12 which develops 600 b.h.p. at 2,100 r.p.m. Like the U.S. AVDS-1790, it is a direct injection engine with an exhaust turbo-blower to each bank of cylinders and it is the only air-cooled tank engine apart from those built in the United States. The use of air-cooling for this and smaller Japanese diesel engines does not, however, signify American influence but a continuation of a long-standing preference of the Japanese Army for air-cooled tank diesels. In fact, the use of air-cooled tank diesels in the Japanese Army goes back as far as 1933, when it was the first to adopt one, in the Type 89B medium tank.

The use of diesel engines has also spread to lighter armoured vehicles. For instance, the British FV.432 armoured personnel carrier and the

FV.433 Abbot 105 mm self-propelled gun are powered by the Rolls-Royce K.60, a scaled down version of the Leyland L.60, which develops 240 b.h.p. and which was developed especially for light armoured vehicles. In this case, however, it has not been always necessary to develop special and inevitably expensive engines, since some sufficiently powerful engines are being produced for civilian purposes. A good example of the more economical use of commercial engines is provided by the U.S. M107, 108, 109 and 110 self-propelled guns which are powered by an adaptation of the General Motors 8V-71T, a 400 b.h.p. V-8, and the M551 Sheridan, which is powered by the 6V-53T, a 300 b.h.p. V-6. Both engines are turbo-charged, water-cooled, two-strokes of the uniflow type with valve-controlled exhaust ports, which makes them less vulnerable than the opposed piston two-strokes with their highly stressed pistons.

The most important consequence of the change to diesel engines has been a substantial increase in the operating range of tanks. This had actually deteriorated in the British and U.S. tanks built immediately after the Second World War, which had a pitifully short operating range compared with the contemporary diesel engined Russian tanks. For instance, Centurions Mark 2 and 3 had a road range of only 65 miles and the U.S. M46 of 70 miles; off-the-road their range was still less. The range was subsequently increased by expedients, such as the attachment of mono-trailers carrying extra fuel to Centurion 5 and the mounting of external, unarmoured, jettisonable fuel tanks on the U.S. M48. A more satisfactory improvement was produced by the redesign of engine installations and hulls, which made room for larger internal fuel tanks. Thus, the road range of the Centurion 7 went up to 115 miles and that of the M48A2 to 160 miles. However, even this was low compared with the operating range which was achieved by changing to diesels, due to their greater thermal efficiency and the higher density of diesel fuel. In terms of the volume of fuel, the change increased the overall operating efficiency from about 20 ton-miles per gallon, or less, to about 30 and this, together with further increases in the capacity of the fuel tanks, gave the M60A1 a road range of 300 miles and the Leopard 350 miles.

In at least one respect, however, there is room for further improvement and that is in the specific output of tank engines. Of the two facets of this problem, specific volume is far more important than specific weight, because the engine compartment occupies about 30 per cent of the space inside the hull and the hull accounts for some 30 per cent of the total weight of the tank, whereas the weight of the engine may represent as little as 2 per cent of the total. In other words, the bulk of the engine installation has a far more important influence on the weight of the tank than its weight and what is needed are engines which occupy the least amount of room in relation to their output.

One type of engine which offers a higher specific output than the diesel is the gas turbine. Investigations into the application of gas turbines to tanks began as early as 1944–45, in Germany, where a lead had already been taken in the use of gas turbines for aircraft. But the original German investigations did not proceed beyond design studies and it was only during the early fifties that the first tank gas turbine engine was built, in Britain, by C. A. Parsons & Co. Ltd. It was a 1,000 b.h.p. unit intended for use in vehicles of the FV.200 series but when it was tried in one its fuel consumption proved very high. This was not altogether surprising at that stage of the development of the gas turbine and the construction of Parsons' engine was premature, which was recognised when further work on gas turbine tank engines was abandoned in Britain for several years.

By 1961, however, sufficient progress had been made with automotive gas turbines to give a more reasonable chance of success to another attempt, made this time by the U.S. Army. A good deal of experience had by then been acquired in the United States through trials of gas turbines in different armoured vehicles, starting in 1955 with Boeing engines, the first American automotive gas turbines, and continuing with the more efficient General Motors GMT-305. Encouraged by its experience, the U.S. Army sponsored in 1961 the competitive development of a 600 b.h.p. gas turbine tank engine by the Solar Aircraft and Ford Motor Companies and, in the meantime, it installed a Solar Saturn 1,100 b.h.p. engine in a T95 tank to gain preliminary experience in the handling of a turbine powered tank. The resulting Ford 705 and Solar T-600 engines offered very much higher specific outputs, on a volume as well as a weight basis, than diesel engines but their fuel consumption was still high and they could not establish an overall advantage over reciprocating engines. Both engines were, therefore, abandoned but in 1966 the U.S. Army placed a contract with the Lycoming Division of the AVCO Corporation for the development of another tank gas turbine, the AGT 1500. This is an engine of about 1,500 b.h.p. which, like the GMT-305 and the Solar T-600, relies on a heat exchanger rather than a high compression ratio for an adequately low specific fuel consumption.

In the meantime a gas turbine was adopted in the Swedish S-tank, but not to power it by itself. Instead, the turbine was combined with a diesel into a two-engine power unit which makes it possible to meet the relatively low average power requirements of a tank with a comparatively small diesel and to use the gas turbine only when additional power is needed. Such an arrangement gets round some of the inefficiency of the gas turbine, particularly at part load,by confining its operation to peak power periods and, at the same time, exploits its high power to volume ratio by making the gas turbine deliver much of the total power needed, infrequently, by the tank. The two engines are geared to a common output but the gear train incorporates free wheels so that either can be used to drive the tank by itself, which reduces the risk of it being immobilised by an engine failure. The gas turbine can also be used as a starter for the diesel, which is particularly useful under very cold weather conditions when gas turbines are much easier to start than piston engines. A two-engine installation is inevitably more complex than a single engine but two reciprocating engines have already been used in many vehicles and most battle tanks carry a second, if much smaller, engine for driving generators and other auxiliary purposes.

The actual engines used in the S-tank are the Rolls-Royce K.60 opposed piston two-stroke diesel of 240 b.h.p. and a simple Boeing gas turbine without a heat exchanger. Originally the turbine was the 502-10MA of 330 b.h.p. but this has been replaced in the production vehicles by the more powerful, 490 b.h.p. 553 model made in Belgium by the F.N.-Boeing Company. The combined output of the two engines gives the S-tank a power to weight ratio which compares very favourably with that of other tanks, particularly since 10 to 20 per cent of the gross output of reciprocating tank engines is lost in driving cooling fans while gas turbines need little external cooling and their gross horse-power is close to their net output. On the debit side the volume of air aspirated by a gas turbine engine is much greater than that of a piston engine of the same power, which makes the installation of adequately large air filters difficult with turbines but the total volume of air required by the two types of engine for combustion and cooling is not very different, so the problem of air louvres at least is much the same.

A more sophisticated but also more difficult approach to combining the advantages of piston engines and gas turbines is represented by compound engines which, in essence, consist of a supercharged piston gas generator coupled to a power producing exhaust turbine. As early as 1950 the U.S. Army sponsored the development by the General Electric Company of the Orion air-cooled, opposed piston gas generator, turbo-compound engine, which was intended to provide a 900 (later 600) b.h.p. power unit for the M47 tank. Development of the Orion was terminated in 1955, before it could be tried in a tank, but other types of compound engines have been under investigation more recently and, in theory at least, their characteristics recommend them for use in tanks. In particular, they offer a high specific output combined with a high efficiency due to the high compression ratio of the piston gas generator, and, like the gas turbines, an almost ideal torque–speed relationship, due to their power being developed at a turbine wheel.

Nevertheless, the overall performance of the diesel engine is not easy to surpass, particularly from the point of view of fuel economy over a wide range of operating conditions, and its competitors are generally more complex as well as requiring a much more advanced level of technology to make them work. Moreover, diesel engines are capable of further development. In particular, they can be supercharged to a much higher degree than they are at present and are capable, therefore, of a much higher specific output. For instance, in 1962 the Caterpillar Tractor Company embarked on the development of a very high output, V-12, four-stroke, turbo-charged, water-cooled engine, the LVMS-1050, which was expected to produce as much as 1,000 b.h.p. out of a swept volume of only 17·2 litres.

The development of the LVMS-1050 was not, however, pursued to a successful conclusion because the interest of the U.S. Army shifted to another type of reciprocating four-stroke, compression ignition engine developed by the Continental Aviation and Engineering Corporation. The essential feature of this engine are hydraulically actuated variable geometry pistons, developed at the British Internal Combustion Engines Research Association, which make it possible to vary its compression ratio from the high value essential for cold starting to a low value determined by the permissible peak cylinder pressure at full load. Because of the reduction in the compression ratio with increasing load, more fuel can be burnt up to a given limit of peak cylinder pressure and, therefore, more power can be produced out of an engine designed to a particular stress level when it is fitted with variable geometry pistons than when it operates with conventional, one-piece pistons. The magnitude of the increase which could be so obtained was demonstrated in 1964, when an AVDS-1100 engine was fitted with the B.I.C.E.R.A. pistons. The AVDS-1100 is a smaller bore version of the V-12 AVDS-1790 and in its standard form it develops 550 b.h.p., or 30·5 b.h.p. per litre, but when converted into a variable compression ratio engine it develops 850 b.h.p., or 47·2 b.h.p. per litre. The use of variable geometry pistons can, therefore, produce a significant increase in the output of diesel engines, particularly in relation to their weight, but it also introduces mechanical complexity where it is least desirable, that is in the pistons. Nevertheless, the Continental Aviation and Engineering Corporation has been awarded a contract by the U.S. Army for the development of a 1,475 b.h.p. variable compression ratio engine for the MBT-70.

The British Army, on the other hand, has taken an interest in the Wankel rotary engine which was developed in Germany, during the fifties, by the N.S.U. Company. In its original form this offers a higher specific output than other four-cycle spark ignition engines but being of that type it brings the development of armoured vehicle engines back to where it was before the general adoption of diesels, as well as introducing mechanical problems of its own. A compression ignition version has already been considered, of course, but so far even the original type of the N.S.U.-Wankel engine has to prove itself superior, overall, to corresponding piston engines.

However, even if it proves successful, the Wankel rotary engine raises the more general question concerning the extent to which it is worth devoting resources to the development of new types of engines, as against building engines of a proved type in a size needed by tanks. The question is made particularly valid by the fact that any new engine which really proves superior will be developed anyway by the automotive industries whereas other components, peculiar to tanks, will not. It might be argued that tanks should not wait for the outcome of industrial developments but the price of technical pioneering is very high and, since the resources available for tank development are not unlimited, what could be spent on speculative work on new types of engines might be far better invested in the development of other components, such as weapons, which the civilian industries will not tackle of their own accord.

By comparison with engines, little effort has been squandered on transmissions whose design has followed general automotive engineering practice. Thus, the crude "crash" gearboxes have been replaced by others with gear-change synchronisers or by automatically controlled epicyclic gearboxes with hydro-kinetic torque converters. The Centurion and the Conqueror have still been fitted with a gearbox where gears are engaged by dog clutches but the Chieftain has an epicyclic gearbox, in which the gears are engaged by means of brake bands, and a centrifugal clutch instead of the simple triple-plate clutch whose operation required considerable foot-effort on the part of the driver. The AMX 30 also has a centrifugal clutch and a gearbox with gear-change synchronisers while the Pz. 61 has a multi-clutch gearbox. American tanks on the other hand, and after them the German Leopard as well as several lighter vehicles, have epicyclic gearboxes with hydro-kinetic torque converters.

The increasing use of hydro-kinetic torque converters is due to their output torque increasing progressively with decreasing output speed to about three times the input torque, at stall, which approaches the torque–speed characteristics required by vehicles. It also eliminates the use of friction clutches, whose life has proved to be particularly short in armoured vehicles, and much of the torque surges associated with gear-changes which increase the risk of immobilisation of vehicles by over-stressing weak ground surfaces. In addition, it also simplifies driving and, consequently, reduces driver fatigue. Unfortunately, the efficiency of the hydro-kinetic torque converter is fairly low and if excessive power losses are to be avoided the torque converter needs to be by-passed as the output to input speed ratio approaches unity, that is as the vehicle gathers speed. The need for this was not recognised in the early applications of torque converters to tanks and, in particular, in the design of the Torqmatic transmission, which was used in the American M26 tank, and the Cross-Drive transmissions which have been installed in several others, from the M46 to the current M60 series. Because of this these early transmissions have not been provided with converter lock-up clutches and as the torque converters remain in operation at all times the transmission losses are considerable. In consequence, the fuel consumption of tanks fitted with the Torqmatic and Cross-Drive transmissions has been high and this, in turn, has given hydro-kinetic torque converters a bad reputation. More recent transmissions are, however, fitted with lock-up clutches and even the Cross-Drive has been provided with one although, surprisingly, the modified, XT-1400 version was still not fitted in the M60 tanks.

In the case of the Cross-Drive, as well as other tank transmissions, the change-speed gears are combined in one unit with steering mechanisms. In the case of the lighter vehicles which can use smaller, industrial transmissions the steering mechanisms are built separately. In either case the steering mechanisms can take one of several forms and as they represent a special problem, which is almost peculiar to tracked armoured vehicles, they are best discussed separately, in the following chapter.

The integration of propulsion and steeering functions has also been a feature of electric and hydrostatic transmissions which have been tried in a number of vehicles. The use of electric transmissions goes back, in fact, to the second French tank design, the St. Chamond of 1916, whereas the torque converter did not come into use until 1940, when it was first installed in the Swedish Strv m/40 light tank. However, electric transmissions have proved heavier and less efficient than mechanical transmissions and their use has been confined to only a few tanks. Hydrostatic tank transmissions are almost as old, since one was tried as early as 1917 in a British Mark IV tank, but they have proved even less efficient and, in spite of periodic attempts to use them, none has gone into service, so far.

The chief attraction of electric and hydrostatic transmissions has been their ability to provide an infinitely variable drive with the output torque increasing hyperbolically with decreasing speed, as required for vehicle propulsion. A hyperbolic torque–speed relationship can only be approximated to by a mechanical, geared transmission but, given five to six speeds, the desired characteristics can be closely approached with it. A well-designed mechanical transmission can also provide a sufficient range of torque multiplication, and speed reduction, to cover the wide spectrum of conditions over which tanks operate and thus make it possible to use the available engine power effectively.

But while the available engine power cannot be fully exploited without an adequate transmission the converse is not necessarily true. In particular, when it comes to operation over rough ground the available power may not be fully usable because of the limit imposed on the speed of tanks under such conditions by the pitching and bouncing which their crews can withstand. Thus, as a result of the limited vibration tolerance of their crews, the maximum speed which tanks can attain over rough ground is limited by their ride characteristics rather than the power to weight ratio and transmissions.

The ride characteristics of tanks depend on their configuration and their suspension. In general, the longer they are the higher is their maximum attainable speed but their length is restricted by steering considerations. To be precise, if tanks are to be steerable, the length of track in contact with the ground cannot exceed 1·8 times the distance between the centre lines of the tracks. In consequence, the ride, and therefore the maximum attainable speed of tanks over rough ground, depend very largely on the extent to which their suspensions can absorb the irregularities of the ground surface.

To minimise the effect of the irregularities of the ground surface on

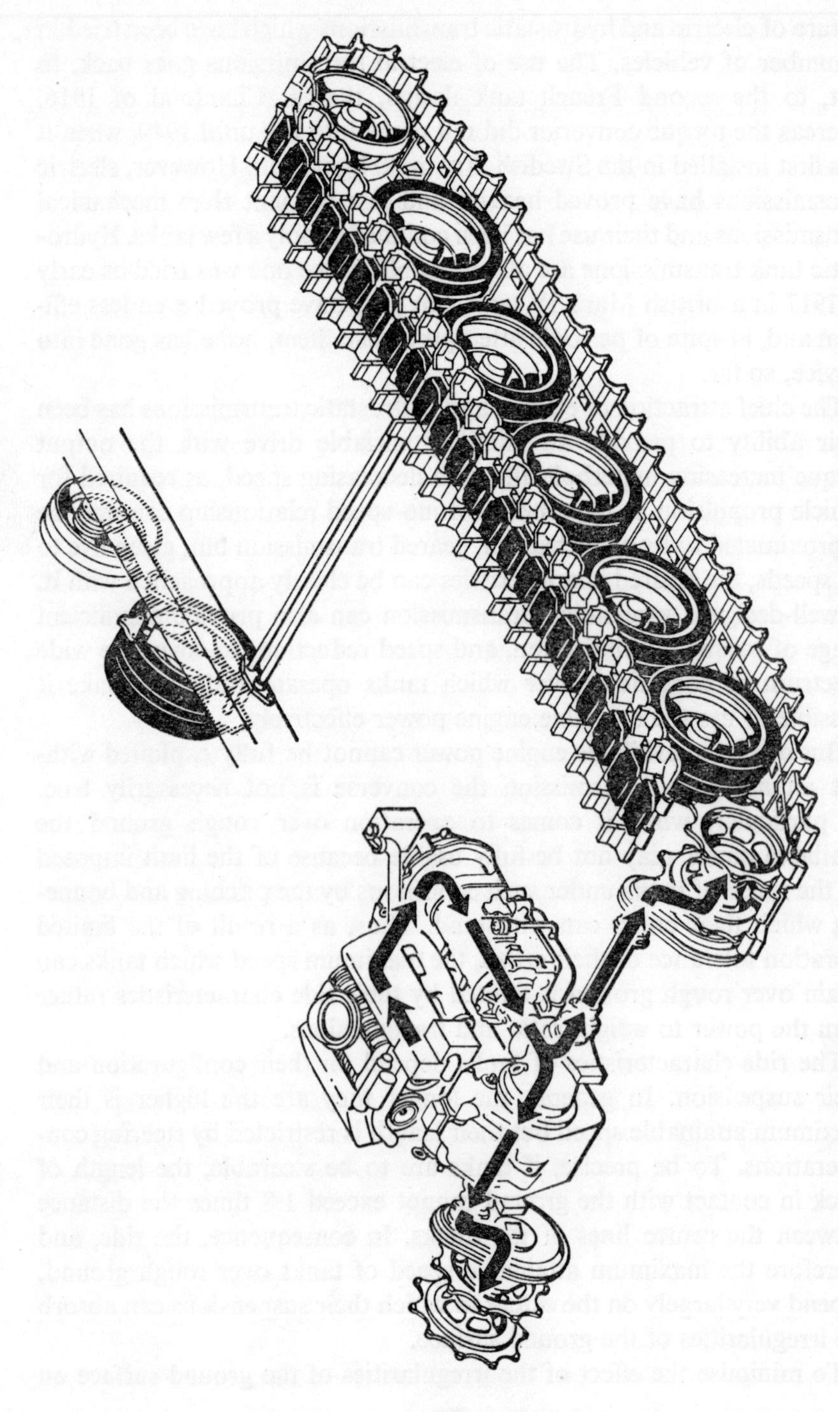

Fig. v Track and torsion bar suspension layout of the U.S. M113 armoured personnel carrier.

the vehicle the suspension needs to provide for large amplitudes of road wheel movement and for attenuating the forces transmitted by the road wheels to the hull. Adequately large wheel displacements can be achieved with bogie suspensions in which wheels are mounted in pairs and react on each other. Suspensions of this type absorb the irregularities of the ground surface mainly by articulation but they only function as intended at relatively low vehicle speeds: at high speeds they are unable to follow the contours of the ground surface. In consequence, although bogie suspensions of the Horstmann type have still been used in the Centurion, Conqueror and Chieftain, almost all other vehicles have road wheels which are independently suspended.

The most widely used type of independent suspension consists of trailing arms to locate the road wheels and transversely mounted torsion bars, which lend themselves to a neat, well-protected installation (Fig. v). Transversely mounted torsion bars take up, however, a significant amount of space within the armour envelope and thus increase the weight of tanks. They also add to the height of the hull and interfere with the location of floor escape hatches. In the last two respects they are inferior to the coil springs of the original type of independent suspension developed during the twenties by J. W. Christie (Pl. 98). But the springs and bell-crank levers of the Christie suspensions occupied more room in the sides of the hull and they have not been used beyond the British Comet of 1944 and the Russian T-34. From the weight and other points of view it is best to mount the suspension externally. This is done with the Horstmann bogie suspension but it is more difficult to achieve in a satisfactory fashion where the wheels are independently suspended (Pl. 99). Rubber-in-torsion springs have been tried in the U.S. T92 and a few other vehicles but only with limited success; a much more satisfactory solution has been adopted in the Swiss Pz.61 where each wheel is sprung by a stack of Belleville washers or disc springs. Springing of this type was to be used in the German E-series tanks, which were being designed in 1944–45, because of its ability to store a large amount of energy in relation to the size, but the Pz.61 is the first tank to be fitted with it.

The best type of springing is one which not only can absorb a large amount of energy in relation to its size but which is also progressive, being "soft" for small deflections and stiffening up at large deflections. Such variable rate characteristics are possessed by hydro-pneumatic springs, which can also be made adjustable and thus offer several additional advantages. For instance, adjustable hydro-pneumatic suspensions can easily provide a variable ground clearance, which at its maximum improves the ability to negotiate muddy terrain and at its minimum reduces the height of the target presented by the tank. Provision for differential adjustment of the suspension units makes it possible to alter the attitude of the hull, and thus elevate or depress the armament, and the suspension units can also be locked, to provide a more stable gun platform. All these possibilities have already been exploited in the S-tank whose fixed gun mounting would hardly have been practicable without an adjustable hydro-pneumatic suspension, and they have also been explored in experimental versions of the U.S. T95 tank.

An adjustable hydro-pneumatic suspension is inevitably more complex than one with metallic springs but far more complicated systems with automatic ride control have already been considered by the U.S. Army. The automatic ride control is based on the use of acoustic, or other, types of sensors which provide information about the height and hardness of obstacles in front of the vehicle; this information is fed into a computer which controls road wheel actuators so that the wheels are sequentially raised or lowered to follow the contours of the ground surface and the effect of the obstacles on the vehicle and its occupants is minimised.

A more immediate if much more modest improvement in the design of suspension systems is represented by the reduction in the weight of the road wheels. To reduce their weight is not easy because of the very large loads which are imposed on the suspension: at speed peak dynamic loads are twenty, or more, times as high as the static loads and, as a result, the suspension components have to be massive, so that they account for 10 to 20 per cent of the vehicle weight. Nevertheless, a significant weight reduction has been achieved in the U.S. M60 by the use of forged aluminium alloy road wheels and in the French E.L.C. light experimental tank of magnesium alloy wheels. A very interesting although unsuccessful attempt has also been made in the United States to use epoxy-bonded glass fibre wheels (Pl. 100).

Almost all tanks now have double road wheels but lighter armoured vehicles, whose wheels are not so heavily loaded and which have tracks with double guide horns instead of a single central guide, continue to use single wheels. The road wheels have been almost all rubber tyred. the thickness of the solid tyres representing a compromise between the need to provide resilience and to reduce the risk of tyre blow-out due to the hysteresis heating of the tyres. An exception to this has been the

Conqueror and some Soviet tanks which have had steel-tyred wheels with rubber between the rim and the hub. This type of resilient tyre originated with the Russian KV heavy tanks and was subsequently used on the German Tiger II, as well as the Russian IS. It offered the advantage of a higher permissible load per unit of tyre width over the rubber-tyred wheels and, at the same time, it had the advantage of resilience over the primitive solid steel rollers which were still used on the Churchill tanks. But, by comparison with rubber-tyred wheels, it shortened track life.

Only one significant attempt has been made since 1945, in the AMX 50, to employ overlapping road wheels, which were used on the Tiger II, and none to use interleaved overlapping wheels which were a feature of the Panther suspension. Both arrangements are theoretically attractive as they produce a more uniform distribution of loads along the track length and, hence, reduce soil stress concentrations. But in practice the gain is small. Moreover, interleaved road wheels are liable to suffer from mud packing and the simpler overlapping wheels impose undesirable twisting loads on the track; also, both are heavier than the conventional arrangement of wheels.

In all cases the road wheels should have as large a diameter as possible, since this reduces rolling resistance as well as minimising the risk of clogging up with mud, snow or stones. If the wheels are large enough it is also possible to dispense with track return rollers and thus save weight. In spite of this, the use of large road wheels has spread very slowly since they were first demonstrated in the twenties by Christie and even now there are many vehicles which could, and should, have larger diameter road wheels than they do.

Christie's vehicles were also among the first to run with relatively slack tracks but many other designers and users have been loath to follow him, for fear of track throwing when turning, in spite of the fact that rolling resistance increases very considerably with track tension. Rolling resistance also varies with the type of track but the energy losses in all tracks are considerable, so much so that on hard level surfaces the rolling resistance of tracked vehicles is two to three times that of wheeled vehicles.

Until a few years ago almost all vehicles produced outside the United States had simple all-steel tracks with ribbed or recessed links, usually of cast manganese steel, and plain cylindrical pins, commonly induction-hardened. Considering its crude nature and, in particular, its plain pin joints open to the entry of abrasive grit, tracks of this type have performed surprisingly well and even on relatively heavy tanks they have had a life of up to about 1,000 miles. Much longer life has been obtained with tracks having rubber bushed pins and rubber road pads, which have been used since 1934 on almost all U.S. tanks and more recently also on the German Leopard, as well as lighter vehicles produced in several countries. However, the results obtained with such tracks vary. In some cases their life is no better than that of the simple track with plain dry-pin joints but in others, particularly in armoured carriers, it reaches 4,000 miles and may even exceed this figure, in some cases by as much as 100 per cent.

There are two main types of rubberised track. The one used longer in U.S. tanks has a steel backbone of two tubular members connected by webs, which are completely covered with rubber. Steel pins with rubber rings or bushes are inserted into the tubular members so that there are two pins for each track block and the track blocks are joined by means of steel connectors which link adjacent pins on each side of the track. In the case of wide tracks two blocks are used side by side, with two long pins for each pair of blocks, and there is a central connector-cum-track guide, as well as the two outside connectors, for each adjacent pair of track links. Any rotation between adjacent track links, which involves rotation between the pins and the track blocks, is taken up by torsion of the rubber bushes. (Pls. 101 and 102).

The second type resembles the conventional steel track in that it has recessed steel links joined by single pins. However, the pin joints are rubber bushed, so that relative rotation is again taken up by torsion of the rubber and not by metal-on-metal sliding. Moreover, there are rubber road pads and the track links are usually rubber backed as well. In several ways, this type of track represents an intermediate solution between the crude but relatively cheap and light all-steel track and the double-pin rubber block type, which is heavy and extravagant of rubber. The latter has also proved inferior to steel tracks in very hot desert areas, because of blow-outs of its thick rubber sections, and on rocky terrain or hard frozen ground. On the other hand, rubber bushed and rubber padded tracks have proved superior whenever a significant amount of road operation is involved, not only because they last longer under such conditions and produce less noise but also because rubber pads give better adhesion than steel ribs on hard ice and wet road surfaces. In addition, rubber pads reduce the damage to roads, so much so that they have now been fitted to the steel dry-pin tracks of tanks such as the Chieftain, the AMX 30 and the S-tank.

However, in cohesive clay soils rubber padded tracks produce less traction.

In the light of all this, steel tracks with rubber bushed pins and removable rubber pads offer the most attractive solution. Bonding of pads eliminates the risk of pads flying off due to the slackening of the retaining bolts of the removable pads but, at the cost of increased maintenance, the latter have the advantage that they are easy to replace and make it possible to revert, when required, to a steel-surfaced track. Further advantages accrue from rubber coating of the backs of track links, which helps to prolong tyre life, reduces still further the transmission of shock loads and reduces the danger of the freezing-in of tracks in cold weather operation. But there are also disadvantages to the rubber coating of link backs in the form of increased rolling resistance and higher cost.

Lighter vehicles can also be fitted with steel cable reinforced rubber belt type tracks, whose development goes back to the French Citroën-Kegresse vehicles of the twenties. Tracks of this type offer the advantages of lighter weight, lower rolling resistance and smoother, quieter operation but their strength is limited and they are more vulnerable to damage. In consequence, their use has been limited in general to vehicles of less than 10 tons, although they have also been tried on some heavier vehicles, such as 16-ton U.S. T92 tank (Pl. 103).

Whichever the type, tracks need to be as wide as possible to keep to a minimum the pressure exerted by the vehicle on the ground. The higher this pressure the greater is the depth to which the tracks sink into soft ground and the greater, therefore, is the amount of work done in propelling the vehicle or, in other words, the higher is the resistance to its motion. The softer the ground the more pronounced is this effect so that a typical vehicle which needs 0·2 h.p./ton per m.p.h. on concrete, requires 0·6 on sandy soils and as much as 1 h.p./ton per m.p.h. on soft clay soils. At the same time the propulsive thrust which a vehicle can generate at the ground is limited by the soil shear stresses. Thus, given a combination of high track pressure and a weak soil, a situation is easily arrived at where the resistance to motion exceeds the thrust which can be generated from the soil. When this happens the vehicle is stalled and its tracks can only churn up the soil excavating ruts until it bellies.

The extent to which the pressure exerted by the vehicle on the ground can be minimised by widening the tracks is, unfortunately, limited by the required width of the hull. In consequence, the stresses imposed by armoured vehicles are higher than is desirable for operation in many types of terrain and far too high for some weak soils. This is particularly true of heavy vehicles which exert higher pressures than light ones, because the ratio of vehicle weight to track ground contact area increases with weight.

The pressures which vehicles exert on the ground are generally defined by the "nominal ground pressure", the quotient of gross vehicle weight and the sum of the products of track width and of its length in contact with the ground. In terms of this, pressures range from about 7 lb/in^2 for light tanks and carriers to 14 lb/in^2, or more, for battle tanks. So far as soils are concerned, the nominal ground pressure should not exceed 10 lb/in^2 if vehicles are to perform adequately in muddy terrain or soft sand, and if it exceeds 13 lb/in^2 they are likely to experience difficulties under such conditions.

The nominal ground pressure is, of course, only a crude approximation to the normal stresses at the track to ground interface. The actual stresses vary considerably along the length of the track, attaining maximum values under the road wheels. On smooth, hard road surfaces the contact area is clearly limited to the surface of the projecting track ribs or road pads but the normal stresses are even higher than this would indicate because the loads carried by the road wheels are concentrated on the track links immediately under them. This can lead to pressures on the surface of the road pads of as much as 250 lb/in^2 although, if reasonable rubber road pad life is to be achieved, the pressure corresponding to the wheel load acting on one link should not exceed 150 to 200 lb/in^2.

In addition to spreading the weight of vehicles over as large a ground contact area as possible and providing traction, tracks are also used in many instances to propel armoured vehicles in water. To improve their propulsive effect in water tracks have had side vanes added to them but the scope for modifications in this respect is limited by the conflicting requirements of operation on land. Greater improvements have been achieved by fitting side screens along the top run of the track and a cowl over the front of it, so that the water carried forward by its top run is directed towards the rear and thus contributes to the forward thrust. Nevertheless, the propulsive efficiency of the tracks is low and the maximum water speed of armoured vehicles is only 4 to 5 m.p.h., unless they are specially designed for amphibious operation at the expense of their performance on land. This has been done in the case of the Landing Vehicles, Tracked, or LVTs, developed for the U.S. Marine Corps, some of which have attained speeds of up to 7 or 8 m.p.h. Moreover, the LVTs can operate in rough waters and even negotiate Pacific surf, which none of the amphibious vehicles designed only for crossing inland waters can. The development of the LVTs goes back to an amphibian designed in the thirties by D. Roebling for rescue work in the Florida Swamps and their production to July 1941, when the first LVT1 was completed by the F.M.C. Corporation. Their current versions are the LVTP5 personnel and cargo carrier and the LVTH6 armed with a turret-mounted 105 mm howitzer, both of which were produced during the early fifties (Pls. 104 and 105).

Propellers suitably driven from the engine provide a more efficient means of propulsion than tracks but they are vulnerable to damage on land and it is difficult to locate them so that the flow of water over them is not obstructed by other parts of the vehicle. As a result, propellers have been used less frequently in recent years than before the Second World War. In contrast, an increasing number of vehicles has been fitted with water jet propulsion units which consist essentially of a ducted propeller mounted in the rear of the hull and suitably driven from the engine. The water jet propulsion units are far less vulnerable to damage than propellers but they occupy a considerable amount of space and add weight (Pls. 106 and 107).

To be able to float, armoured vehicles need to have sufficient buoyancy but only those which are large in relation to their weight can be made to have it without the use of additional flotation gear. Apart from the LVTs, vehicles which can float without preparation are exemplified by the Russian PT-76 light tank, which is propelled by a water jet propulsion unit, and the U.S. M113 armoured personnel carrier, which is track propelled. Heavier vehicles can not, however, be made to float without additional equipment.

The most popular type of flotation equipment consists of a collapsible fabric screen carried permanently on the vehicle. Equipment of this type originated in Britain with N. Straussler, who developed it from the basis of collapsible, canvas-hulled assault boats. It was first tried in June 1941, fitted to a Tetrarch light tank, and was first used, with limited success, during the Anglo-American amphibious landing in Normandy, on June 6, 1944, fitted to M4 Sherman tanks. Its use after the war was confined to experimental vehicles but during the past few years it has been adopted on the S-tank, and the Vickers 37-ton battle tank, as well as several lighter vehicles (Pl. 108).

A similar type of flotation screen can be used for heavy battle tanks but in this case its size prevents it being carried permanently on the vehicle and it needs to be supported, to prevent it collapsing in rough water. An example of this is provided by the equipment developed for the 50-ton Centurion (Pl. 109). It consists of sealed decking at track guard level on which the vehicle crew erect twelve light weight reinforced plastics sandwich panels—four at each side and two each at the front and rear. The panels are supported by spring loaded bolsters and straining ropes all connected to a single blow-out pin located at the top of the turret and are sealed by a water-proofed fabric cover which is rolled up over them like a corset. Its total weight is about 1500 lb. and it can be jettisoned by blowing off with a small explosive charge.

This type of equipment enables tanks to float even in relatively rough off-shore waters and is well suited, therefore, to use in amphibious landing operations. It represents, however, a relatively clumsy and slow method of crossing rivers and other inland water obstacles. When erected it makes the tank very conspicuous, since its overall height is 12 ft, and the crew need at least 15 minutes to erect it.

A better method of crossing inland obstacles is by deep or submerged fording. The Leopard and the AMX 30 have been designed so that they can operate in water with only the tops of their turrets showing (Pl. 110). All the preparation they require for this is the operation of a switch which causes all the air to be taken in through the commander's hatch. The depth of water which these tanks can ford can be increased further, to about 15 ft, by fitting an extension tube to the turret. This has been done on the U.S. M60, as well as the AMX 30, and the tube is large enough for the tank commander to stand at the top of it, so that he can control the movement of the tank. The tube also provides an alternative dry escape route (Pl. 111).

A different approach to submerged fording has been adopted on the Russian T-54. Like the other tanks it is suitably sealed but the air intake takes the form of a relatively small diameter two-piece metal tube which is erected, with the aid of cable stays, on top of the turret prior to a crossing. Thus, when the T-54 crosses a river underwater only the top of this tube shows above the surface and its movement is controlled by radio from the river bank. Work on the conversion of tanks to submerged operation started in Britain, at the Experimental Bridging Establishment, as early as 1939, and in May 1940, a modified A.9 (Cruiser Mark I) tank made a successful underwater crossing of the River Stour but soon afterwards the project was abandoned. At about the same time work of a similar nature started in Germany in connection with Operation Sea Lion, the projected invasion of the British Isles. The idea underlying this work was that tanks would be launched from landing barges standing some distance off-shore and approach the beaches underwater. The tanks themselves were Pz. Kpfw. III and IV suitably sealed and provided with air and exhaust tubes. The feasibility of operating them underwater was demonstrated by the end of June 1940, but as the invasion never took place they were only used in the crossing of the River Bug on June 22, 1941, the opening day of the German campaign against Russia.

Provision for submerged operation was subsequently incorporated in the design of the Tiger I but the underwater crossing of rivers was not practised on any scale until the introduction of the T-54 into service with the Soviet Army. The maximum depth at which battle tanks can operate submerged is limited to about 18 ft by the difficulty of sealing them at greater depths. Tanks operating underwater also face the problem of developing sufficient traction while they experience a lift equal, according to Archimedes' principle, to the weight of fluid they displace, which can be only partly alleviated by flooding the engine compartment. Nevertheless, the ability to operate underwater to a depth of 15 to 18 ft, enables tanks to cross many water obstacles and greatly increases their operational mobility.

CHAPTER 6

Steering of Tracked Vehicles

THE steering of tracked armoured vehicles represents a peculiar and interesting engineering problem which demands closer scrutiny. It centres on the fact that all but a few tracked vehicles have been built with laterally rigid tracks. In consequence, they have been steered by creating a difference between the thrusts generated by the tracks at the ground and thereby obtaining a turning moment which slews the tracks and turns the vehicle.

One major consequence of the use of laterally rigid tracks and the associated skid-steering methods is that it confines the configuration of tracked vehicles within relatively narrow limits of the ratio of length to width or, to be more precise, of the ratio of the length of the track in contact with the ground to the distance between the centre lines of the tracks. In fact, if tracked vehicles are to be manoeuvrable, this ratio must lie within the narrow range of 1·1:1 to about 1·8:1, because of the magnitude of the resistance to track slewing in relation to the maximum longitudinal thrust which a track can generate. As a result, tracked vehicles cannot be made as long as would be desirable both from the point of view of high speed movement over uneven hard surfaces and of reducing the ground pressure to improve their performance on soft ground. Moreover, on soft ground, when the soil under the track is stressed close to failure, the slewing moment necessary for steering can only be obtained by reducing the thrust of one track, since it is not possible to increase that of the other. Thus, steering is accompanied by a reduction in the total forward thrust and in weak soils may lead to a complete immobilisation of the vehicle.

To overcome the shortcomings of laterally rigid tracks and skid-steering, a few attempts have been made to steer by bowing tracks in the ground plane but the difficulties associated with laterally flexible tracks, which are necessary, and the complication of the track setting mechanisms have worked against the adoption of this method. It was tried as early as 1921 by Lt. Col. P. Johnson in the Light Infantry Tank which had laterally flexible "snake tracks" with lubricated spherical joints but these proved troublesome, and curved track steering only came into limited use during the thirties. The most successful example of its use, so far, has been provided by the Tetrarch light tank designed in 1936 at Vickers-Armstrongs Ltd. under the direction of L. F. Little. The Tetrarch and its war-time successor, the Alecto self-propelled gun, incorporated a complete system of track setting by pivoting all four road wheels on each side and could perform large radius turns by track curving alone. This was accomplished with a conventional type of track, laterally flexible to the extent permitted by the clearance between the track pins and the holes in the track links. The use of curved track steering produced a significant improvement in the overall efficiency of the two vehicles due to the elimination of much of the power losses associated with skid-steering but the latter still had to be used for tight turns and the complication of the track setting mechanism has not been considered justifiable in more recent designs.

Instead, there has been a revival of interest in articulated vehicles, whose manner of steering may be regarded as an approximation to curved track steering and which can dispense with skid-steering altogether. Thus, while curved track steering involves bowing the whole length of the track in contact with the ground, the turning of articulated vehicles involves, in essence, disposing two or more laterally rigid tracks so that their centre lines are at an angle to each other and thereby approximating to the curving of laterally flexible tracks. In general, articulated vehicles have been built with two units, each unit having two tracks like a conventional tracked vehicle.

The first articulated tracked vehicle, a lorry, was built in Britain in 1913 by B. J. Diplock but it was only around 1950 that the development of this type of vehicle really began, in Canada and the United States, due largely to Lt. Col. M. G. Bekker, who became an advocate of it as a result of his researches into soil-vehicle mechanics and, in particular, because it could be made longer in relation to its width than a conventional tracked vehicle. In consequence, a number of special-purpose articulated cargo carriers has been built since the mid-fifties and they have proved the superior performance of this type of vehicle over snow and muskeg or peat bogs. Since 1951 a number of design studies has also been carried out to ascertain the feasibility of articulated armoured vehicles but none has been able to establish that they would be superior, overall, to more conventional vehicles. Their potential advantages are essentially the same as those of other articulated tracked vehicles, namely higher average cross-country speeds because of their greater length and reduced risk of immobilisation due to their lower ground pressures and articulated steering. However, their disadvantages include greater weight, greater shipping length, inferior manoeuvrability in confined spaces and mechanical complication and, put together, these outweigh their advantages.

Thus, tracked armoured vehicles are built with two laterally rigid tracks and are skid-steered, which means that they need to have some form of track control to slew the tracks. The most obvious and also the least efficient method of producing the required difference between the thrusts of the two tracks is to drive them independently of each other by means of separate engines, which was actually done in the British Medium A tank of 1918. A more sophisticated but still inefficient method is to have each track driven by a separate electric or hydrostatic motor, power being supplied to the motors from an electric generator or hydrostatic pump coupled to the vehicle's engine. Both alternatives have been tried but, with the exception of a few tanks with electric transmissions, all tracked armoured vehicles have been steered by mechanical means.

Steering mechanisms have taken several different forms and they are best considered divided into two groups, according to their principal functional characteristics. Thus, one group is made up of differential mechanisms and their derivatives, in which the drive is transmitted continuously to both tracks, and these will be examined first. The other group consists of clutch-and-brake and geared steering systems, in which the drive to the tracks is discontinuous and which will be examined later.

The simplest and earliest form of a differential steering mechanism consists of interposing a simple differential in the drive to the tracks and having an independently operated brake at each output half-shaft, as shown in Fig. VI. The application of one of the brakes reduces and eventually reverses the torque at the corresponding track sprocket, creating a difference between the ground forces acting on the tracks, and, consequently, a turning moment necessary to slew the vehicle.

A system of this kind was incorporated in the first successful fully tracked vehicle, the tractor which was built in 1905 in Britain by Richard Hornsby and Sons, Ltd., of Grantham, and which was the subject of Patent No. 16 345 granted a year earlier to D. Roberts. Braked differential steering was also incorporated in the very first British tanks, from Little Willie of 1915 to the Mark IV of 1917, but the differential was normally locked out and the tanks were steered by other means, as will be described later. Thereafter, braked differential steering was used in a number of very light vehicles, notably in the Carden Loyd tankettes of the late twenties and their descendant, the Bren Gun Carrier, which was produced on a large scale during the Second World War. Since then this type of steering has been virtually abandoned, in spite of its advantage of simplicity.

The reason why the use of the braked differential was, by and large, confined to a number of light vehicles is that it proved less efficient than any other steering mechanism. This arises from the fact that the power generated by the inner track during a turn cannot be transferred by a braked differential to the outer track and that a large proportion of the

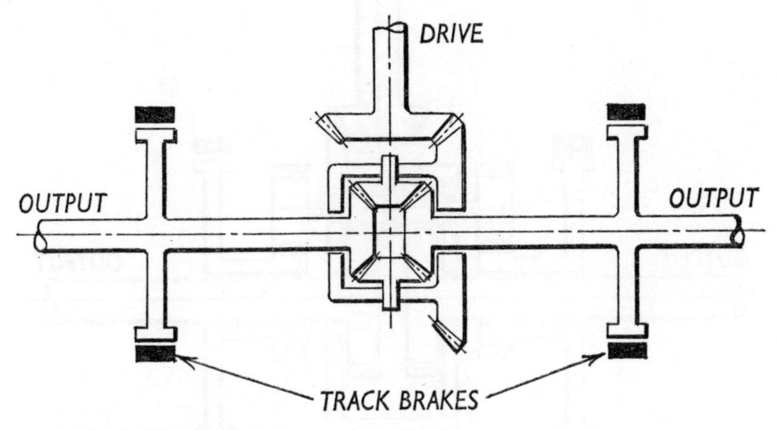

Fig. VI Braked differential.

engine power is dissipated in the steering brake. In other words, a braked differential system is non-regenerative and engine, as well as inner track, power are dissipated in the steering brake while it is slipping. When the brake is locked all the engine power is transmitted, of course, to the outer track but turns under these conditions are only practicable at very low vehicle speeds.

The major disadvantages of the braked differential are overcome in the closely related controlled differential. In this no attempt is made to bring the inner output shaft to rest by the application of a steering brake but only to a fraction of the mean speed of the two shafts by adding supplementary gears to a simple differential, as shown in Fig. VII. In a mechanism of this kind no engine power is wasted in the steering brakes and, what is more, power generated by the inner track during a turn is transferred to the outer track, which helps to supply the power required by that track and makes the system regenerative.

The controlled differential first appeared in 1916. In that year a patent application for it was filed in the United States and the first tractor was built with it. The original U.S. Patent, No. 1,253,319, was actually issued in 1918, to R. H. White and was assigned to the Cleveland Tractor Company, of Euclid, Ohio, which built the first tractor with controlled differential steering. In consequence, this form of steering has commonly been called "Cletrac" steering, after the trade name adopted by the

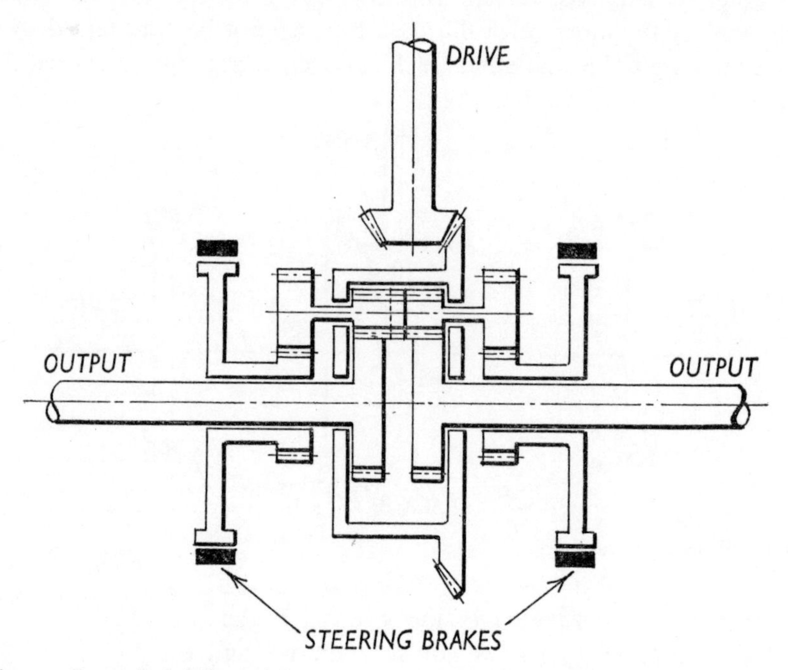

Fig. VII Controlled differential.

Cleveland Tractor Company, while in France it is generally known as the "Cleveland" differential. It has also been described as the "geared differential" but it is most widely known as the "controlled differential", which seems the most appropriate designation.

The first tank to have been fitted with a controlled differential appears to be the Renault NC light tank built to a French Army requirement in 1926. Subsequently almost all light tanks built in France up to 1940 were provided with this form of steering which has reappeared there since 1949 in the AMX 13 light tank family. In the United States it was first installed in 1932, in the T1E5 light tank, and was then used in almost all U.S. armoured vehicles up to the end of the Second World War in 1945, from light tanks to the heavy, 85-ton T28.

Controlled differential steering has reappeared in the United States during the past fifteen years in the M59 and M113 armoured personnel carriers. It has also been adopted in the Japanese Type 61 battle tank, the HS.30 armoured personnel carrier of the German Army and vehicles of the FV.400 family developed for the British Army, including the FV.432 armoured personnel carrier which is the first British armoured vehicle to go into production with this type of steering mechanism.

The reason for the large scale use of the controlled differential is to be found in the combination of reasonable performance and relative simplicity which it offers. In fact, it represents the simplest type of steering mechanism, if one ignores the unsatisfactory braked differential, and one in which one pair of brakes can be used not only for steering the vehicle but also for stopping it, when both brakes are applied simultaneously.

However, the controlled differential also has a number of shortcomings. One arises from the fact that when the brakes are off it acts as a simple differential, giving a balance between the input and output torques but not fixing the ratio of the output torques, which is governed by the reactions between the tracks and the ground. In consequence, it depends on these reactions being equal for straight ahead motion of the vehicle and when they vary it produces undesirable effects, such as drifting on cambered roads or veering during deceleration. In the extreme, when one track loses traction and spins in muddy terrain or when obstacles are negotiated at an angle, differential action leads to a loss of drive to the other track and stalling of the vehicle.

Another major shortcoming of the controlled differential is that its gearing gives only one minimum radius of turn, which has to be a compromise between the requirements for large radius turns at high speeds and tight turns at low speeds. Large radius turns can, of course, always be made by slipping the brake but this is inefficient and manoeuvrability in confined spaces can only be improved by fitting an additional set of brakes—one to each output shaft. When one of these brakes is applied instead of the normal steering brake the controlled differential behaves like a brake differential. Thus, when the brake stops slipping, a skid turn is obtained about the locked track.

A controlled differential with additional track brakes was first installed in the French AMX 13 light tank developed between 1946 and

1949. Since 1958 it has also been fitted to vehicles of the M113 family developed by the F.M.C. Corporation, and in particular to the M113A1 armoured personnel carriers. In this case an additional reason for the adoption of the supplementary track brakes has been that they improve manoeuvrability when the amphibious vehicles of the M113 series propel themselves in water by means of their tracks.

Whatever its advantages, with or without additional track brakes, the controlled differential can be improved upon by the double differential. This consists of two differentials arranged in parallel and with their output shafts geared together, as shown in Fig. VIII.

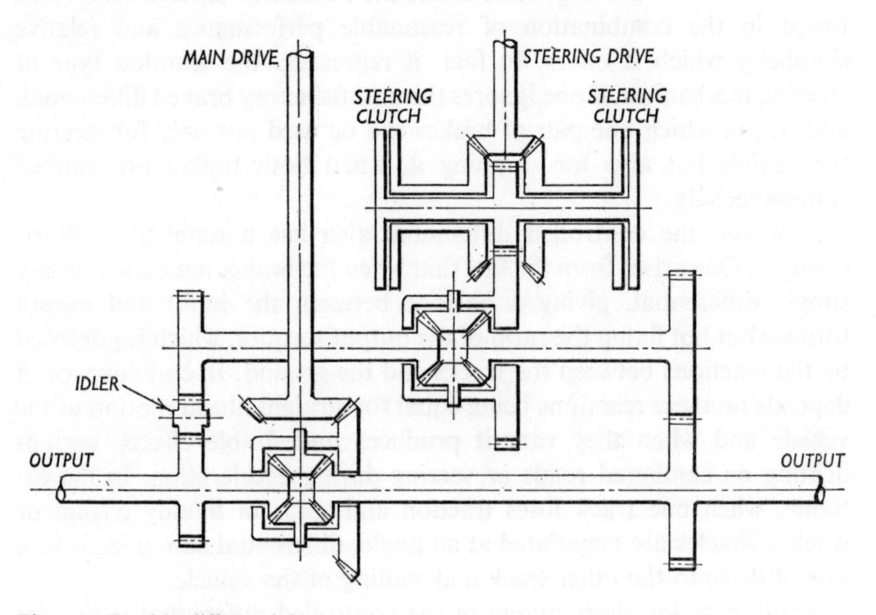

Fig. VIII Double differential.

The two differentials can both be driven from the output of the propulsion gearbox, in which case this system behaves in exactly the same way as the controlled differential. But if one of the differentials is driven, instead, from the input of the propulsion gearbox then the system gives a different minimum radius of turn for each gear in the gearbox, the lower the gear the smaller being the radius, which is generally required.

The relationship between the minimum radius of turn and the speeds at which the main and steering input shafts are driven is best brought out by expressing the ratio of the speeds of the output shafts in terms of the speeds of the input shafts. Thus, from the kinematics of the system,

$$\frac{\omega_1}{\omega_2} = \frac{\omega_M \pm K\omega_S}{\omega_M \mp K\omega_S} \tag{6.1}$$

where ω_1 and ω_2 are the speeds of the output shafts, ω_M and ω_S are the speeds of the main and steering input shafts, respectively, and K is a constant depending on the gearing.

This equation shows clearly that the smaller the value of ω_M the greater is the ratio of the output shaft speeds and, therefore, the smaller the radius of turn. It also shows that when the propulsion gearbox is in neutral and the steering drive is engaged, that is when $\omega_M = 0$ and $\omega_S \neq 0$, a pivot turn is achieved, with one track going forwards and the other one backwards, giving exceptional manoeuvrability in confined spaces.

A double differential steering mechanism was first built in France and very much earlier than is generally believed. The original mechanism was, in fact, designed at the Schneider Company under the direction of E. Brillié for installation in the SRB experimental battle tank whose development started in 1921 and in which the double differential was first demonstrated in May 1924. The same system was subsequently adopted for the type B battle tank, the first prototype of which was completed in 1929 and the first production models in 1936.

In the original form in which it was installed in the SRB and B tanks the double differential was actually more sophisticated than the mechanism shown in Fig. VIII, as it had a Naeder hydrostatic motor-pump set in the steering drive from the input of the propulsion gearbox, instead of the steering clutches. The hydrostatic steering drive gave an infinity of turning radii for each gear of the propulsion gearbox, with the radii varying continuously from the smallest possible radius in one direction to the smallest radius in the other and straight running in the middle of the range. Moreover, in its mid-position it held the steering input shaft stationary thereby preventing differential action between the tracks when running straight ahead.

The mechanism shown in Fig. VIII is a simplified version of the original system which was installed in the S-35 medium tank designed in 1934 by the Société d'Outillage Mécanique et d'Usinage d'Artillerie, or S.O.M.U.A. In this the hydrostatic steering drive was replaced by a mechanical drive with clutches which engaged the steering input shaft as required for a right or left turn. At other times the steering input shaft was free so, in contrast to the type B, the tracks were differentially driven and there was, of course, none of the infinitely variable control provided by the hydrostatic drive.

Development of the original form of the double differential steering mechanisms was brought to an end by the defeat of France in 1940, but in the meantime equivalent mechanisms began to be developed in Britain and in Germany. The design of these was based on two epicyclic gear trains in parallel, one at each output shaft, with the annuli driven from the output of the propulsion gearbox and the suns driven in opposite senses by a steering drive engaged by one of the two steering clutches, slowing down one output shaft and speeding up the other to give a turn in the required direction.

The simplest form of such a mechanism is shown in Fig. IX. When

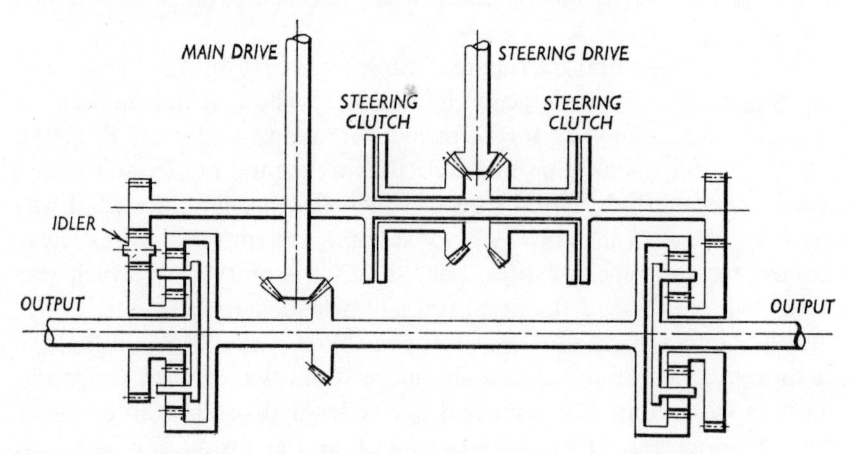

Fig. IX Epicyclic equivalent of the double differential shown in Fig. VIII.

the steering clutches are disengaged the cross shaft connecting the sun gears balances the torques acting on them, which results in a balance of output shaft torques, as with a conventional differential. In fact, the mechanism shown in Fig. IX is kinematically equivalent to that shown in Fig. VIII, and so, among others, equation (6.1) is equally applicable to it. In other words, it is basically a double differential and is best referred to as such, although mechanisms of this kind have also been called "controlled epicyclics" and "controlled differentials".

The first double differential of this kind was designed in Britain around 1928 by Major W. G. Wilson. Instead of the steering clutches shown in Fig. IX, it had two three-speed epicyclic gearboxes and as the propulsion gearbox had six forward speeds it gave 3 × 6 turning radii. It also appears to have incorporated a brake for holding the steering cross-shaft fixed so as to prevent differential action between the tracks when driving straight ahead.

The original design was never translated into practice but in 1938 Dr. H. E. Merritt, then at the Woolwich Arsenal, revived the development of double differential steering mechanisms and designed one which was similar in principle to that proposed by Wilson. As before, the steering drive was taken from the input of the propulsion gearbox but it had only two speeds and as the propulsion gearbox had seven forward speeds it gave 2 × 7 turning radii. The propulsion gearbox was actually of Maybach design, which led to the whole system being called the Merritt-Maybach transmission.

One such transmission was eventually installed in the A.16 E.1 experimental heavy cruiser tank and at least one more double differential system was designed in 1940 at Rolls-Royce Ltd. But, in the meantime, Merritt developed a triple differential system and it was this which was adopted in British tanks, in the shape of the Merritt-Brown transmission.

Double differential systems were, however, adopted in Germany where their development appears to have started in 1937, with experimental transmissions tried in Pz.Kpfw. I and II light tanks. This was followed, in 1939, by the Henschel L.320 C transmission designed for the experimental VK 3001 medium tank. The L.320 C transmission had three speeds in the steering drive but this was taken from the output of the propulsion gearbox, so that there were only three turning radii. Full advantage had obviously not been taken in this early design of the potentialities of double differential systems but this could not be said of its derivatives, the Henschel L.600 C and L.801 transmissions built for the Tiger tanks between 1942 and 1945. In these the steering drive was taken from the input side of the propulsion gears and the number of speeds in it was reduced from 3 to 2, though with an eight-speed gearbox this still gave 2 × 8 turning radii.

Since then transmissions with double differential steering have also been developed in the United States. They evolved, curiously enough, from attempts to combine features of the Merritt-Brown triple differential with a hydro-kinetic torque converter. The first of the resulting transmissions was designed in 1943 by O. K. Kelly and G. Hause of the General Motors Transmission Products Study Group and it was first demonstrated in May 1944, in an M26 tank. The development of what became known as the Cross-Drive transmission was transferred in 1945 to the Allison Division of General Motors, where the Model CD-850 was put into production in 1949. This was first installed in the M46 medium tank of that period and a modified version, the CD-850-6, is still used in the M60A1 battle tank.

A smaller version of the Cross-Drive was also developed. This is the Model CD-500, which has been installed in the M41 light tank and its

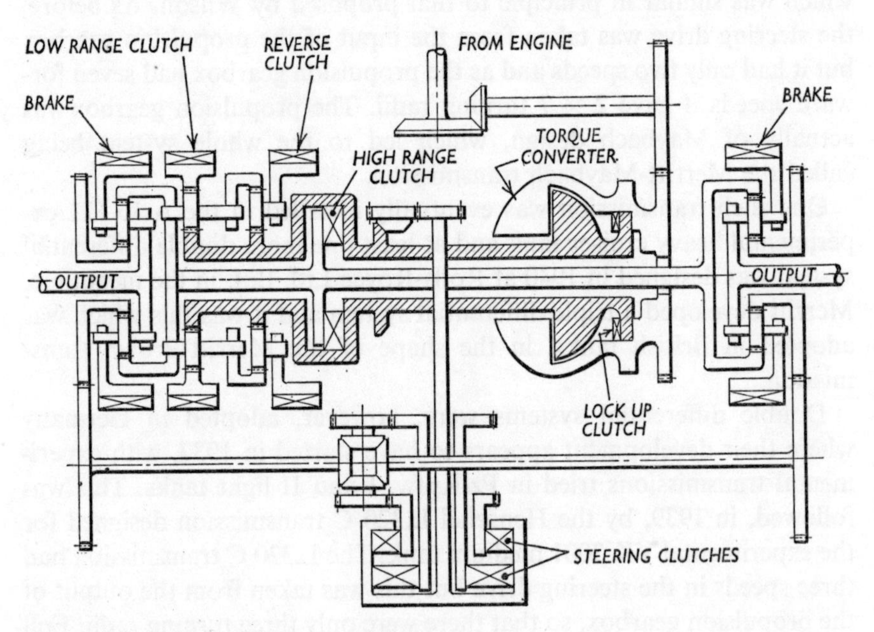

Fig. x Allison Cross Drive transmission.

derivatives. The general construction of the Cross-Drive is indicated in Fig. x.

A somewhat similar transmission with a torque converter and double differential steering has also been developed during the fifties in Germany for the Leopard battle tank by the Zahnradfabrik Friedrichshafen AG. It differs, however, from the Cross-Drive, as well as the earlier Merritt-Maybach and Henschel transmissions in having a mechanical interlock between the sun wheels of the epicyclic trains on each side, which eliminates differential action when driving straight ahead.

A double differential system has also been adopted in the Pz. 61 battle tank designed during the mid-fifties in Switzerland, at the Eidgenössische Konstruktionswerkstätte Thun under the direction of

T. W. Ludwig. In this case the steering drive is through a hydrostatic pump-and-motor set, which gives all the additional advantages already mentioned in connection with the original double differential steering system of the French SRB and B tanks. A double differential with a hydrostatic steering drive has also been adopted in the HSWL 123 transmission developed by Renk AG for the *Jagdpanzer* (*Kanone*) built by Rheinstahl Hanomag AG.

The last of the differential systems developed so far is the triple differential shown in Fig. XI. It is very similar functionally to the double

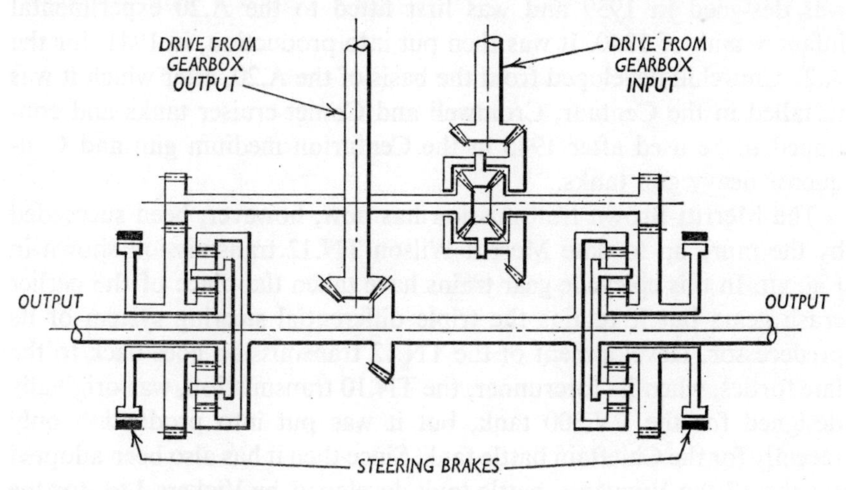

Fig. XI Triple differential.

differential and has much the same advantages and disadvantages. Thus, it is regenerative and, if the steering drive is taken from the input side of the propulsion gears, it gives radii of turn which decrease as the propulsion gears are shifted down, as well as a neutral or pivot turn. However, as can be seen from a comparison of Fig. IX and Fig. XI, steering control is exercised by means of brakes instead of clutches, which might be considered an advantage. On the other hand, power is transmitted by both input shafts during straight ahead running and not only when steering, as in the case of the double differential. This and the way in which a difference between the speeds of the output shafts is achieved does not make the triple differential suitable to the application of a hydrostatic drive, to achieve progressive steering control. It also lends itself less readily than a double differential to the installation of a differential lock, which would prevent differential action between the tracks, with all its disadvantages, when driving straight ahead.

There are two versions of the triple differential. In one the sun gears of the epicyclic trains at the output shafts rotate in the same sense as the annuli. In consequence, in this system, engine power is simply split between the main drive to the annuli and the steering drive to the suns and then re-combined in the epicyclic. In the other system the sun gears rotate in the opposite sense to the annuli, so that power is recirculated from the suns to the main drive.

The original triple differential system incorporated in the Merritt-Brown transmission was actually of the second kind. This transmission was designed in 1939 and was first fitted to the A.20 experimental infantry tank of 1940. It was then put into production, in 1941, for the A.22 Churchill developed from the basis of the A.20, after which it was installed in the Centaur, Cromwell and Comet cruiser tanks and continued to be used after 1945 in the Centurion medium gun and Conqueror heavy gun tanks.

The Merritt-Brown transmission has now, however, been succeeded by the more up to date Merritt-Wilson TN.12 transmission shown in Fig. XII. In this epicyclic gear trains have taken the place of the earlier crash gears but it retains the triple differential steering system of its predecessor. Development of the TN.12 transmission goes back to the late forties, when its forerunner, the TN.10 transmission, was originally designed for the FV.300 tank, but it was put into production only recently for the Chieftain battle tank. Since then it has also been adopted for the 37-ton Vijayanta battle tank developed by Vickers Ltd. for the Indian Army.

The first triple differential system without recirculation of power appears to have been developed in Sweden, at A.B. Landsverk. It was originally adopted in 1949, in the Bofors-Landsverk IKV 72 assault gun and it continues to be used in its development, the IKV 103. A triple differential system has also been developed since the late fifties for the French AMX 30 battle tank.

The earliest of the second group of steering mechanisms is represented by the clutch-and-brake system. The basic features of this system are shown diagrammatically in Fig. XIII. Steering is effected by disengaging one of the clutches, which disconnects the drive to the track on its side, and the subsequent application of the corresponding brake to slow down the undriven track still further. When the brake stops slipping a skid turn is obtained about the locked track, as with a braked differential. However, no engine power is dissipated in the track brakes, as it is in a braked differential, all of it being transmitted during a turn to the one

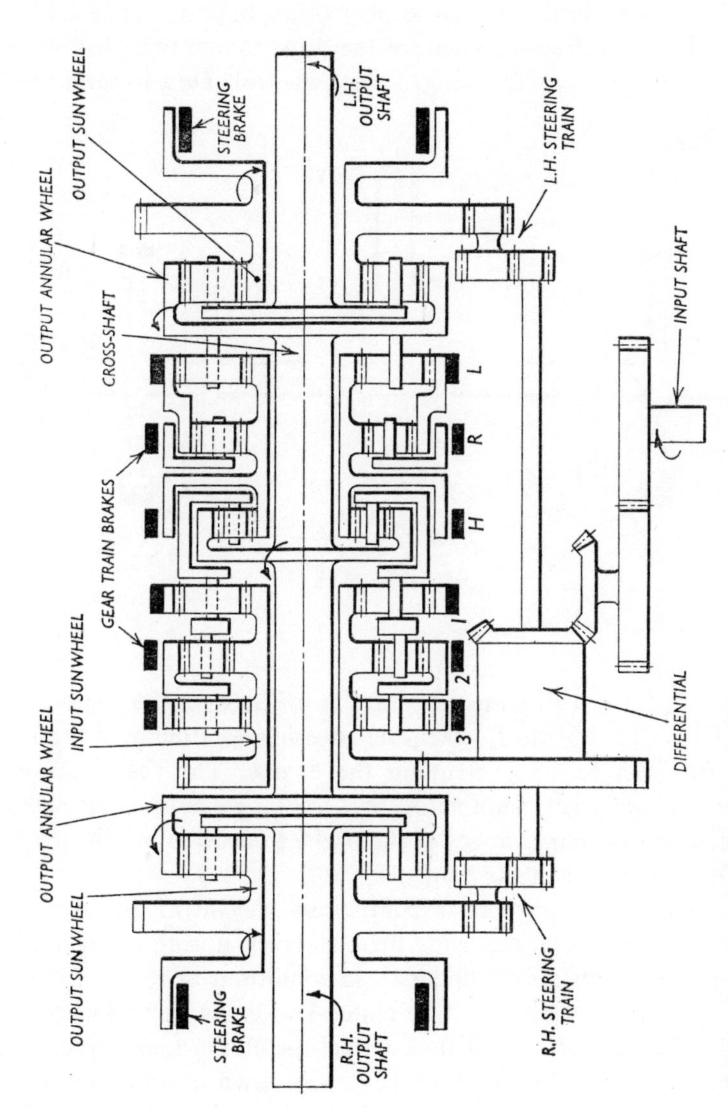

Fig. XII Merritt-Wilson TN.12 transmission.

driven track. But power generated by the inner track is still dissipated in the brake and, as none of it is transferred from the inner to the outer track, the clutch-and-brake system is clearly non-regenerative.

The clutch-and-brake system is also discontinuous, since initiation of a turn involves disengagement of the drive to one track followed by the engagement of another form of track control. This, in turn, implies

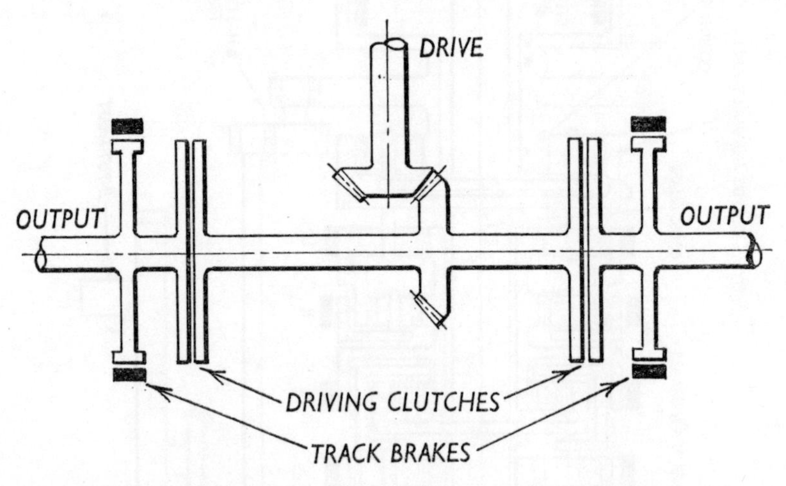

Fig. XIII Clutch-and-brake system.

the risk of reversed steering, i.e. turning in the opposite sense to that expected by the operator, whenever steering is attempted while the vehicle happens to be overruning the engine. The risk of reversed steering can be largely eliminated by arranging the disengagement of the clutch and the engagement of the brake to overlap but this requires a careful adjustment of the controls.

The instability inherent in discontinuous systems at the commencement of steering contrasts with their stability during straight ahead running and the instability under these conditions of most of the continuous, differential systems. The clutch-and-brake system also differs from the differential system in a reduction of the mean track speed during a turn, because one track is slowed down whereas the other is driven at the same speed as before. This is in contrast to all the differential systems where the slowing down of one track is accompanied by a corresponding speeding up of the other track and the mean speed of the two tracks remains constant. A reduction in the mean track speed is a disadvantage when it comes to small steering movements, as it implies an undesirable slowing down of the vehicle, but it is an advantage when rapid changes of direction are required, since the change in the momentum of the vehicle helps to initiate the turn.

In addition to all this, clutch-and-brake systems have also enjoyed the advantage of relative simplicity. In consequence, they have been used more widely than other systems.

The first appears to have been devised in the United States, by B. Holt, who first demonstrated it in November 1904, in a half-track tractor built by the Holt Manufacturing Company, of Stockton, California. Following the example of Holt tractors, clutch-and-brake steering was adopted in 1916 in the first French tanks built by the Schneider Company. Clutch-and-brake methods were also generally employed when steering the first British tanks of 1916 and 1917: the differential fitted to these tanks was usually locked out and to steer one of the auxiliary gearboxes in the drive to each track was put into neutral after which the track brake on the same side was applied.

Clutch-and-brake steering systems were almost universally used during the twenties and continued to be used during the thirties not only in light but also in medium and heavy tanks. Typical examples of their large scale use were provided by British light tanks from the Vickers Carden Loyd Mark VIII of 1928 to the Light Tank Mark VI of 1936, the German Pz. Kpfw. I and the Russian T-26. They were also used in heavier tanks, such as the Vickers Medium designed in 1922, the A.1 Independent heavy tank and the early cruiser tanks, up to the Mark IV of 1939, as well as the Matilda and Valentine infantry tanks of that period; they were also used in all Russian medium and heavy tanks, from the BT and T-35 of the early thirties to the T-34/85 and the KV 85 produced towards the end of the Second World War.

In tanks as heavy as the 52-ton KV 2 clutch-and-brake steering systems proved unsatisfactory and they were, in fact, the most troublesome component of the Russian heavy tanks. But in vehicles with high power-to-weight ratios and adequately large brakes they have proved reasonably satisfactory, a very recent example of this being provided by the new Swedish armoured personnel carrier, the Pbv 302, designed by A. B. Hagglund & Soner. The Russian PT-76 amphibious reconnaissance tank and its derivatives are also believed to be fitted with clutch-and-brake steering.

It has often been argued, of course, that the discontinuity inherent in the operation of this system makes it particularly unsuitable where power-to-weight ratios are high and the vehicles are, consequently, capable of high speeds. In practice, however, a well designed system, such as that of the Pbv 302, can provide satisfactory steering at up to about 40 m.p.h.

In addition to the simple clutch-and-brake system, there has also been the variant shown in Fig. XIV. In this the disengagement of the drive to the tracks is effected by releasing the reaction member of the

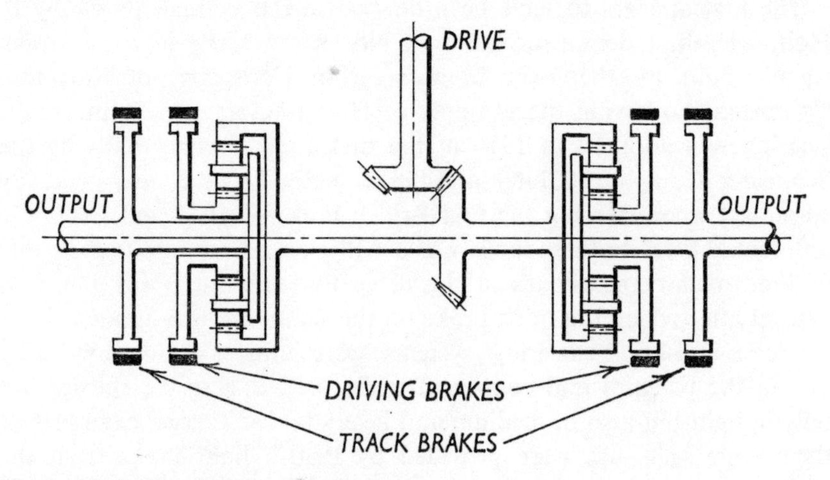

Fig. XIV Epicyclic clutch-and-brake system.

epicyclic final drive reduction gears, after which a track brake is applied as before.

The first system of this kind was designed in Britain in 1916, by Major W. G. Wilson and was demonstrated in March 1917, in a modified Mark IV tank before being put into production in the Mark V. After the First World War it fell into disuse, except for some experimental models, but during the thirties it reappeared on a large scale in the German Pz. Kpfw. III and IV medium tanks and in Italian tanks, from the L.3 tankette to the M 13/40 medium. Since the end of the Second World War it has, however, suffered another eclipse.

At least one major disadvantage of the clutch-and-brake system is overcome if, instead of disconnecting the drive to one of the tracks and trying to bring that track to rest, one track is merely driven at a lower speed than the other. This can be accomplished by having a two-speed set of gears in the drive to each track and changing down on one side or the other, which gives a regenerative system since power generated during a turn by the inner track is transferred, through the gears, to the outer track. Driving the tracks at different speeds also provides larger radius turns than those possible with the clutch-and-brake system, except by the inefficient process of brake slipping.

In other respects the characteristics of a geared system resemble those of the clutch-and-brake system. Thus, like the latter, it is discontinuous, provides a positive drive to both tracks during straight ahead running and gives a lower mean track speed during a turn. Its one disadvantage is that it cannot provide turns as tight as the skid turn obtainable with the clutch-and-brake system and it has, in almost all cases, been used in combination with the latter, to give a two-phase steering system of the kind illustrated in Fig. xv.

In principle, the first British tanks, up to and including the Mark IV, were provided with geared steering as they had a two-speed gearbox in

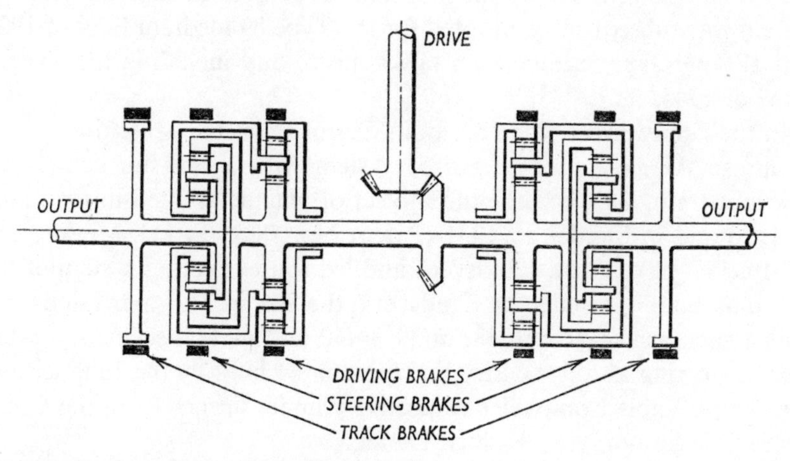

Fig. xv Wilson's geared steering system.

the drive to each track. In practice, however, they were steered by clutch-and-brake methods, as already described. The first practical geared system was designed in 1918 by Major W. G. Wilson for the Anglo-American Mark VIII heavy tank. This had a two-speed epicyclic gearbox in the drive to each track and was steered by changing down on one side to obtain a geared turn or, if a tighter turn was required, by releasing both epicyclics, thereby disengaging the drive, and applying the track brake to obtain a skid turn, as in any clutch-and-brake system. The gears were also shifted down simultaneously to lower forward speed and whenever this was done the system could only act as an epicyclic clutch-and-brake system.

No further interest was shown in Britain in geared steering until

1927–28 and even then only one or two geared systems were built, to Wilson's design, for the experimental A.6 Sixteen-tonner tanks. Ten years later, in 1938, another geared systems was designed under Wilson's direction for the prototype of the Matilda infantry tank but it was only in 1940 that a similar system finally went into production, for the Covenanter cruiser tank, and this system is actually the one illustrated in Fig. xv. The same system was subsequently used in the Crusader and Cavalier but in the next cruiser, the Centaur of 1942, it was abandoned in favour of the Merritt-Brown transmission with its triple differential.

In the meantime different geared systems with a single epicyclic train and a multiplate clutch had been developed and adopted in other countries. The earliest of these appears to be the system designed in 1925 by Capt. T. Hara for the first tank to be built in Japan. A similar system was subsequently adopted for the Type 89 medium tank of 1929 and all later Japanese medium tanks, up to and including the Type 5 Chiri of 1945.

In the late twenties work began in Germany, at the Maschinenfabrik Esslingen AG, on another geared system with a two-sun compound epicyclic train. This became the subject of patents granted in Germany in 1930 and in Sweden in 1931 (Patent No. 78,038) to O. Merker and W. Buchegger of A. B. Landsverk and led to the steering system of the first tank built in Sweden by Landsverk, the Strv m/31. Later Landsverk tanks, such as the Strv m/38, m/39, m/40 and m/42 also incorporated geared steering as did the Strv m/37 and m/41 built by the Jungner and the Scania Vabis Companies respectively under licence from the Czech firm of Ceskomoravska Kolben Danek.

The prototype of the Strv m/37, the Praha AH IV, developed around 1934, appears to have been the first tank built in Czechoslovakia with geared steering, which was subsequently incorporated in other and much more successful tanks built by Ceskomoravska Kolben Danek, the LTH and its development, the TNHP or LT 38. This was not only produced in Sweden as the Strv m/41 but was used on a large scale by the German Army during the Second World War and its chassis proved to be mechanically one of the most successful of that period. Its steering system again incorporated a two-sun compound epicylic train and a multiplate clutch.

In 1936 geared steering of yet another type was also adopted, for the first time, in a Skoda tank, the experimental T.21, which was regarded as one of the most promising medium tanks on the eve of the Second World War.

Since 1945 geared steering has also been adopted in Russian tanks such as the T-54 medium tank, and more recently still in the United States. It is of interest to note that geared systems have been developed in the United States to replace in part at least the earlier Cross-Drive transmissions, with their double differential steering systems, on which the U.S. Army had concentrated in the late forties.

The first of the new United States transmissions, developed since the early fifties by the Allison Division of General Motors, actually only incorporated clutch-and-brake steering. But, although transmissions of this kind were fitted to a number of prototypes, vehicles adopted for production have since been fitted with transmissions providing geared as well as clutch-and-brake steering. A good example of this is provided by the current 105 mm self-propelled howitzer which in its T195 prototype form was fitted with a transmission of the original XT series, the XT-300-2, with clutch-and-brake steering only. But the production model of the same vehicle, the M108, has been fitted with a transmission of the XTG series, the XTG-411-2A, which has been developed since the mid-fifties and which incorporates geared steering.

However, like the original Wilson epicyclic geared steering system of 1918, the Allison transmissions of the XTG series only provide clutch-and-brake steering when in low gear. In high gear, on the other hand, they only provide geared steering. The only earlier development which might be compared with this is the complete elimination of the clutch-and-brake mode of operation in the steering systems of the Landsverk Strv m/38, m/39 and m/40 which, in contrast to their predecessor and their successor, had nothing but geared steering.

The disadvantage of geared steering by itself is much the same as the principal disadvantage of a controlled differential, namely a single minimum radius of turn. In its usual form, combined with clutch-and-brake steering, it is comparable with the controlled differential with additional track brakes. In this case it has the undoubted advantage of clutch-and-brake over the braked differential mode of operation when it comes to skid turns. Otherwise, apart from all the other relative virtues of geared and differential systems, it also has the advantages over the controlled differential of lower energy losses while the brakes are slipping. This is an advantage which geared systems also enjoy over double and triple differentials, while under conditions of no brake or clutch slip there is no difference in efficiency between them and the other regenerative systems.

An obvious refinement of geared steering is to use gearboxes with more than two speeds in the drive to each track, to obtain more than one minimum radius of turn. The first attempt at such multi-geared steering is represented by Wilkins' Clutch Gear designed in Britain in 1916. One transmission of this type was demonstrated in a modified Mark IV tank in March 1917 but it was never put into production. The first successful multi-geared system was installed in the third of the Sixteen-tonners, the A.6 E.3 built by Vickers-Armstrongs Ltd. in 1929. It was designed by Major W. G. Wilson and consisted of one six-speed epicyclic gearbox in the drive to each track: steering was effected by changing down to a lower ratio on one side than on the other and vehicle speed was changed by simultaneous gear changes in the two boxes.

A similar scheme was tried once again in 1939, in the A.14 experi-

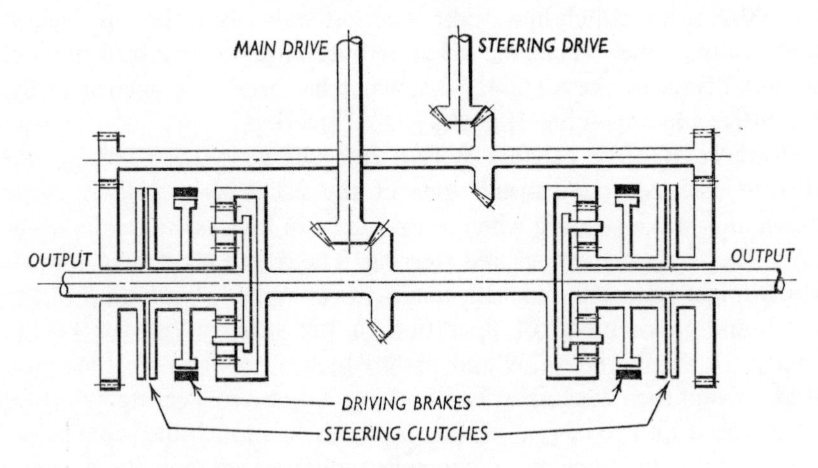

Fig. XVI Multi-geared steering system of the Panther tank.

mental heavy cruiser where Wilson's epicyclic step-down steering was carried to the extreme of an eight-speed gearbox in the drive to each track. This was obviously a cumbersome arrangement and it was not developed further.

A much more elegant form of multi-geared steering was devised in 1942 at the Maschinenfabrik Augsburg-Nürnberg AG for the German Panther medium tank of that period. The M.A.N. system is shown diagrammatically in Fig. XVI and consists of an epicyclic train at each output shaft with the annuli of the epicyclics driven from the output of the propulsion gearbox and the sun gears fixed for straight running by the brakes. To steer the brake on one side was released and the clutch on that side engaged, so that the sun on that side was driven in the opposite sense to the annulus and the speed of the corresponding output shaft was reduced. Since the drive to the suns came from the input to the propulsion gearbox there were as many minimum radii of turn as there were speeds in the gearbox, which in the case of the Panther was seven.

Moreover, when the propulsion gearbox was in neutral and one of the steering clutches was engaged the output shafts were driven in opposite senses, giving a pivot turn. Apart from being simpler, the

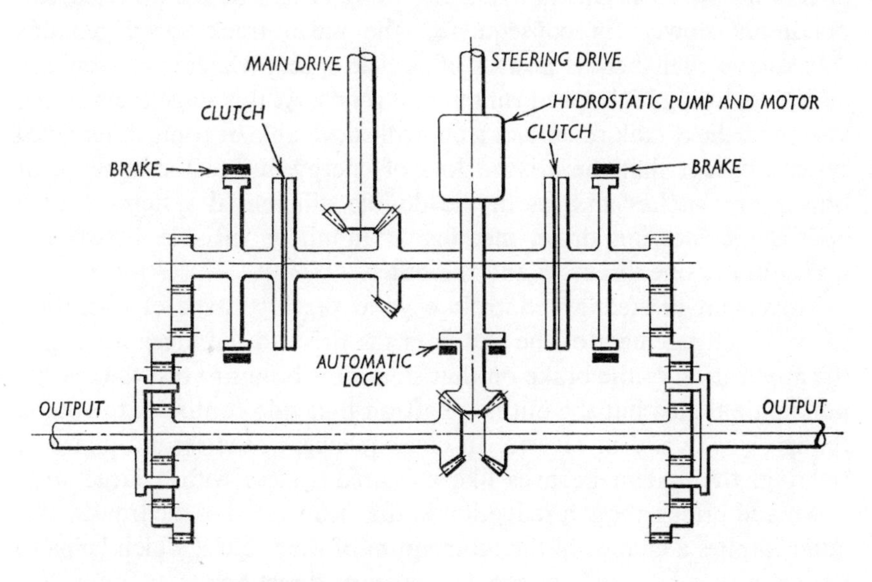

Fig. XVII Steering system of the S-tank.

M.A.N. system also had the advantage over the Wilson multigeared system of a much shorter path, not involving the propulsion gears, for the transfer of power generated by the inner track to the outer track. For all this, the M.A.N. multi-geared system appears to have been used so far in only one other type of vehicle, the French AMX 50 experimental battle tank of the early fifties.

The latest type of steering system is shown in Fig. XVII, and it combines, appropriately enough, some of the best features of the differential and geared systems. It was devised by S. Berge and S. Henstrom, and it has been developed since 1956 by the Bofors Company for the S-tank.

When running straight, the output shaft of the hydrostatic steering drive shown in Fig. XVII is held stationary and so are the suns of the epicyclic trains at the output shafts with the result that there is no differential action between the tracks. This makes for directional stability and is particularly advantageous in muddy terrain or when negotiating obstacles at an angle since a loss of traction by one track, which might occur under such conditions, does not bring about a loss of traction by the other track.

Steering is effected in two stages. The first movement of the steering controls causes the hydrostatic drive to rotate the suns in opposite directions, which results in one track going faster and the other correspondingly slower. In consequence, the mean track speed remains constant so that there is no loss of vehicle speed, which is particularly desirable during high speed running on roads. At this stage the steering system of the S-tank resembles a controlled, double or triple differential system, except that there is no loss of energy due to the slipping of brakes or clutches and, as in the double differential systems with a hydrostatic steering drive, steering is infinitely variable between a maximum in one direction and the other.

Movement of steering controls beyond the first stage of operation causes disengagement of the clutch in the drive to the inner track and the application of the brake on that side. This brings to rest the corresponding annulus but the output shaft on that side continues to rotate, though slowly and in reverse. In consequence, in the second phase of steering, the system behaves like a geared system with a large step-down and brings about a reduction in the mean speed of the tracks. The latter implies a change in the momentum of the vehicle, which helps to initiate a turn and leads to rapid changes of direction.

In contrast to geared systems, and the first stage of operation, there is, however, no regeneration of power in the second phase of operation, because the inner track is driven in the same direction as the ground forces acting on it. But as the second stage of operation is used far less frequently than the first and generally for short periods of time its non-regenerative nature is not a handicap.

When the main drive is disengaged and both track brakes are applied the annuli of the epicyclics are fixed but the suns can be turned in opposite directions by the steering drive to give a positively controlled pivot turn. This means that the ratio of track speeds is fixed and equal to —1, instead of being dependent on the reaction of the ground on the tracks, as it is in double or triple differential systems—which steer instead of executing pivot turns when the reactions experienced by the two tracks differ.

Finally, in the event of failure of the hydrostatic drive, or of the diesel engine to which it is coupled, the steering shaft is automatically locked so that the S-tank can not only be driven by its second, gas turbine engine but it can also be steered with the system operating in a simple clutch-and-brake mode.

CHAPTER 7

Evaluation of Tank Designs

TANKS are evidently so complex as to admit of more than one solution to a given problem. In consequence, there are alternative designs which have to be evaluated, either to assess the relative merits of existing vehicles or to choose the most promising approach.

A common response to the need to evaluate alternative tank designs is to compare, one by one, their individual features, such as gun calibre, vehicle weight and maximum speed. This can be of value but it does not get one very far in evaluating designs as a whole, because the tank is not a mere aggregate of individual components but an integrated system of interacting elements.

Another reaction to the existence of alternative designs are general arguments about their "fire-power", "mobility" and "protection". Invoking these three traditional concepts helps to clarify discussions by emphasising three major facets of tank design but is of little help in evaluating tanks as a whole. For one thing, "fire-power", "mobility" and "protection" do not lend themselves to a precise definition. Moreover, it is by no means clear how the attributes covered by "fire-power", "mobility" and "protection" are inter-related and how, therefore, they could be combined into an overall assessment.

In either case, therefore, the evaluation of tank designs is largely a matter of personal opinions and subjective judgements. To advance beyond them it must, clearly, start from different and more fundamental considerations.

The basic question in the evaluation of tank designs is how successful the different tanks might be on the battlefield. Any answer to this implies the prediction of their battlefield performance. But, in view of the inherent complexity of the problem, performance on the battlefield can not be predicted exactly. What can be done, however, is to estimate the chance, or probability, that the tank will perform a battlefield mission and then to compare the effectiveness of different designs on that basis. The advantage of such a probabilistic approach is that it places the evaluation of tank designs on a more precise, quantitative basis and, consequently, that it makes assessments more objective.

If tanks are going to be assessed on the basis of the probabilities of success in performing their battlefield mission this needs to be clearly defined. Numerous attempts have already been made to do this in terms of "breaking through enemy positions", "infantry support", "exploitation", "offensive combat", and so on, but although these might have described the roles of tank units they do not define what precisely is the battlefield function of the individual tank. Another and more precise definition needs to be adopted, therefore, which leads to the conclusion that the tank's mission is essentially to destroy all major battlefield targets within visual range.

Of the battlefield targets which the tank is expected to engage the most difficult consists of hostile tanks. In consequence, the ability to destroy, or "kill", hostile tanks has become the criterion of the tactical effectiveness of tanks. The adoption of this criterion implies that tanks which are effective against hostile tanks are at least as effective against other targets. This may not always be true but, in general, the ability to destroy other tanks is a satisfactory primary criterion of the effectiveness of tanks. In consequence, the evaluation of tank designs reduces to the determination of the probabilities of success in destroying hostile tanks.

The general approach to determining the probability of success for a complex operation, such as that involving a tank on the battlefield, is to break it down into a sequence of independent events. Having done this, the next step is to determine the probability of the occurrence of each event. Then, multiplying these probabilities together gives the overall probability of success, i.e. a quantitative statement of the chance that the tank in question will successfully accomplish its mission.

The simplest sequence into which the achievement of success against a hostile tank may be broken consists of three consecutive events. The first is arriving in time within striking distance of the target. The second is surviving to engage the target. The third is inflicting lethal damage by engaging the target. If the probabilities of the occurrence of these three events are P_A, P_S and P_K, respectively, then the overall probability of success, P_{SS}, is given by:

$$P_{SS} = P_A \times P_S \times P_K \tag{7.1}$$

It is evident that for the overall probability of success to be high all three probabilities making it up need to be high or, in other words, that a high probability of the occurrence of two events can be largely nullified by a low probability of the third. For instance, a tank which has a high kill probability P_K and a high probability of survival P_S will, nevertheless, have a low probability of success if it has a low probability P_A of getting within time and range of the target, which is generally associated with a low overall "mobility".

However, to calculate the probability of success, it is necessary to consider the problem in greater detail, since each of the three events leading to equation (7.1) is itself made up of a sequence of events. Thus, the achievement of a kill when a target is engaged involves, first, hitting the target; second, given a hit, perforating its armour; third, given a perforation, inflicting lethal damage. There are, therefore, three probabilities to consider and since they are bound to be determined for the weapon system functioning as intended the probability of this happening needs to be considered also. In consequence, the determination of the kill probability P_K involves four other probabilities, i.e.

$$P_K = P_H \times P_P \times P_L \times P_R \tag{7.2}$$

where P_H = hit probability
P_P = probability of perforating armour, given a hit
P_L = probability of lethal damage, given a perforation
P_R = probability of the weapon system functioning correctly.

Of the four, hit probability follows directly from the fact that the pattern of the points of impact of a number of projectiles fired from a tank gun can be described by a probability density function of the distances (x, y) from the impact points to the centre of the vertical target at which the gun is aimed. This function is generally assumed to be a bivariate normal distribution which, when integrated over the target area, gives the probability of a hit,

$$P_H = \frac{1}{2\pi\sigma_x\sigma_y} \iint_A e^{-\left[\left(\frac{x-x_m}{\sigma_x}\right)^2 + \left(\frac{y-y_m}{\sigma_y}\right)^2\right]} dx\, dy \tag{7.3}$$

where A = area of the target,
x_m = mean horizontal error, i.e. the horizontal distance between the aiming point and the mean impact point,
y_m = mean vertical error,
σ_x = standard deviation of the distribution of horizontal errors, i.e. of the horizontal distances between the aiming point and the impact points,
σ_y = standard deviation of the distribution of vertical errors,

and the vertical and horizontal errors are statistically independent of each other.

The above mathematical model clearly relates hit probability to four parameters of the distribution of impact points, namely the two mean errors, which define the position of the mean impact point, and the two standard deviations, which characterise the dispersion of the impact points about the mean. The magnitude of these four parameters is the result of a number of component errors and they increase with distance.

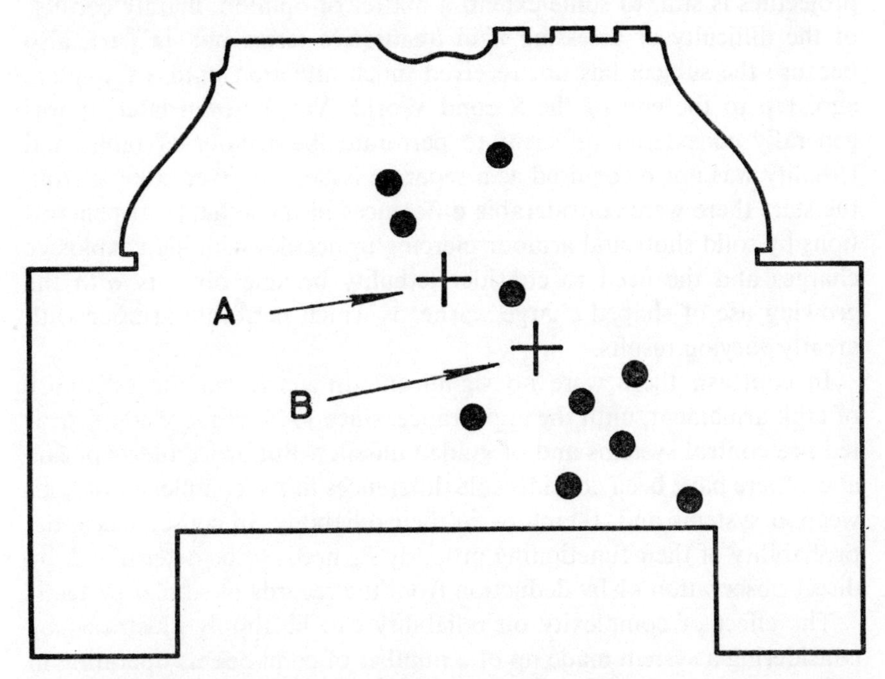

Fig. XVIII Pattern of hits on a stationary target under ideal range conditions, where A represents the aiming point and B the mean impact point.

In general, the most important of all the sources of errors is that in the determination of the range to the target, and consequently the elevation of the gun, which makes y_m, the mean vertical error, the dominant parameter of the probability distribution.

Under ideal conditions, and with the distance to the target known accurately, a pattern of ten hits scored at medium range might be as shown in Fig. XVIII, where *A* represents the aiming point and *B* the mean impact point. But under other conditions the distance between *A* and *B* would be considerably greater and so would be the dispersion.

The probability of perforating the armour of a tank depends on the terminal performance of the projectile fired at it in relation to the effectiveness of the armour at the point of impact, which varies over the surface of the tank. The probability P_P cannot, therefore, be expressed as simply as P_H, and in most cases has to take the form of a simple average over some vital area of the tank, such as front of the hull.

The probability of inflicting lethal damage is the most difficult to determine. In fact, the lethality of the different types of armour-piercing projectiles is still, to some extent, a matter of opinion, mainly because of the difficulty of assessing it in qualitative terms but, in part, also because the subject has not received much attention until a few years ago. Up to the end of the Second World War, or even later, it was generally considered sufficient to perforate the armour of tanks and lethality was not recognised as a separate issue. However, almost from the start there were considerable differences in the lethality of penetrations by solid shots and armour piercing projectiles with high explosive charges and the need to consider lethality became obvious with the growing use of shaped charge warheads which perforate armour with greatly varying results.

In contrast, there were no significant differences in the reliability of tank armament, until the appearance, since 1945, of more sophisticated fire control systems and of guided missiles. But, since their appearance, there have been considerable differences in the complexity of tank weapon systems and, therefore, in their reliability. In consequence, the probability of their functioning properly P_R needs to be determined, by direct observation or by deduction from the records of similar systems.

The effect of complexity on reliability can be simply illustrated by considering a system made up of a number of components operating in series, so that the failure of one causes the whole system to fail. Thus, the probability that the system will not fail is given by the product of the probabilities of the components not failing and if there are n components each with the same probability P_C, then

$$P_R = P_C^n \tag{7.4}$$

In numerical terms, a system consisting of ten components, each having a probability of not failing of 0·995, or in other words 99·5 per cent reliable, will have an overall reliability of 0·951. But a more complex system with 100 components, each as reliable as before, will have an overall reliability of only 0·605. In other words, the more complex the system, and the more components it has therefore, the less reliable it is.

The relative magnitude of the probability of hit, of perforation, of lethal damage and of functioning properly, and their influence on the kill probability, are best indicated by considering two alternative battle tank armament systems. One might be represented by a high velocity gun firing APDS shot and a fairly simple fire control system and the other by a guided missile system. Their respective probabilities of success against a stationary target at medium range are tabulated below.

Probability	*Armament System*	
	Gun	*Missile*
Probability of hit, P_H	·70	·80
Probability of perforation, P_P	·70	·80
Probability of lethal damage, P_L	·95	·90
Probability of functioning correctly, P_R	·99	·75
Kill probability, P_K	·47	·43

When the probabilities of the two armament systems are compared, the missile is seen to have a higher hit probability and a higher probability of perforating armour. Yet its kill probability is lower, because of the lower lethality of its shaped charge warhead and its lower reliability. This does not mean that guided missile systems are inferior in all cases to gun armament but it shows how the low probabilities of the occurrence of some events can offset the high probabilities of others and how important it is, therefore, to take them all into account. The kill probability values, which are just below 50 per cent, also indicate that at least two rounds have to be fired at a tank target to destroy it.

The relative position of gun and missile systems depends very largely on range. This is due to the fact that the probability of kill of gun systems is a monotonically decreasing function of range while that of missile systems varies little within their effective range. In consequence, guided missiles are generally superior to guns at long ranges but inferior to them at short ranges. The exact cross-over point is not easy to define but recent estimates put it at between 2,000 and 3,000 metres.

The fall-off in the kill probability of tank guns with range is due principally to the fall-off in their hit probability, which is illustrated in

Fig. XIX. This shows curves of the single shot hit probability of a typical contemporary 105 mm high velocity gun firing APDS projectiles against a target 2 meters wide and 1·8 metres high, which corresponds to the frontal area of the turret and hull of a well-designed medium

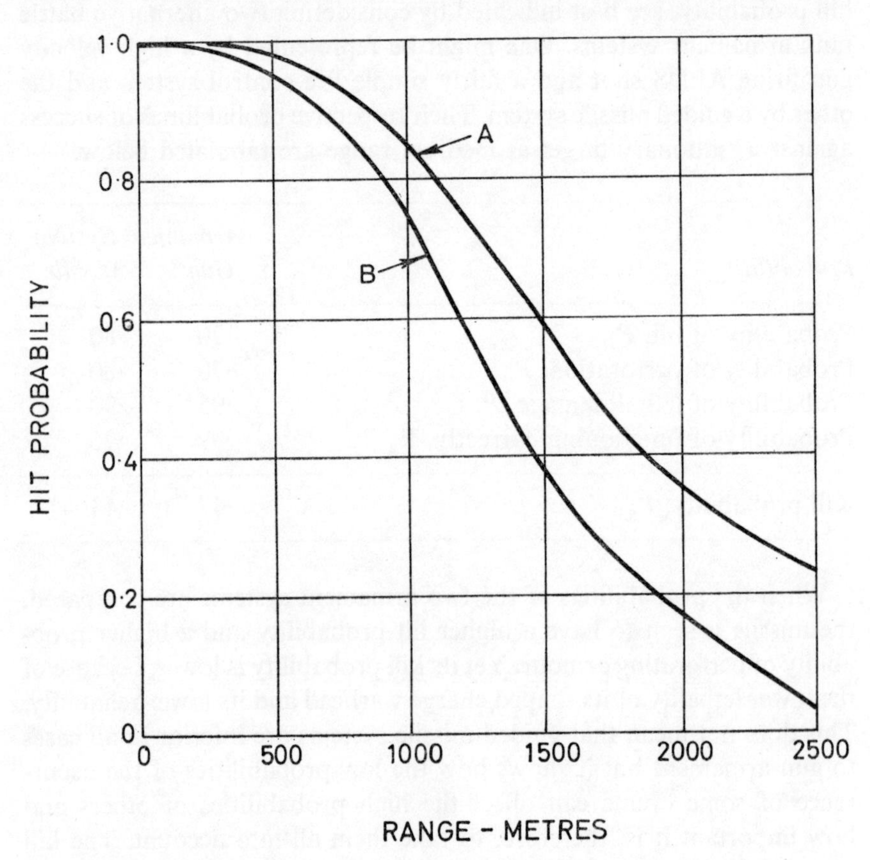

Fig. XIX Single shot hit probability of a typical 105 mm gun firing APDS shot with (A) and without (B) the aid of a range finder.

tank: curve A applies to the case where the gun fire-control system incorporates a range-finder while B applies to the case of visual range estimation, which inevitably involves large errors.

One conclusion which is bound to be drawn from any comparison of the two probability curves shown in Fig. XIX, is that a tank whose performance corresponds to A can engage targets with a given probability of success at longer ranges than a tank whose performance corresponds to B. The advantages which might accrue from such differences in the possible ranges of engagements, or, what is much the same thing, in the probabilities of kill at long ranges can be greatly reduced, however, if the ranges are such that targets are seldom sighted at them. For instance, hit probabilities at 2,500 metres are of small consequence if the relative frequency of the ranges at which tank targets are first sighted follows a normal, bell-shaped distribution with a mean range of 1,300 metres: under such conditions the chances of sighting a target at 2,500 metres are negligible. Thus, the ability to engage targets at long range might not be very valuable and it can even be harmful if it is achieved at the expense of performance at ranges at which tanks most frequently sight each other.

However effective their armament might be, to make use of it tanks need a reasonably high chance of surviving in a battlefield environment. In other words, in addition to a high kill probability they also need a high probability of survival.

The probability of survival is simply the probability of not being killed. Thus, if the probability that an opposing tank will kill the tank in question is P_{K_0}, its probability of survival P_S is given by

$$P_S = 1 - P_{K_0} \tag{7.5}$$

In consequence, many of the points already made in connection with kill probability are equally relevant to the probability of survival. In particular, the probability of the tank being hit by a particular weapon at any given range is given by equation (7.3), which is the integral of the probability distribution function of the projectile or missile impact points over the vertical projected area of the tank. The smaller that area, therefore, the smaller is the chance of the tank being hit. However, in view of the importance of the mean vertical error, which arises from errors in range determination, the chance of the tank being hit decreases much more with reductions in the height of the target area it offers than with any reductions in its width.

The chances of tanks being hit depend also on the skill of their commanders in exploiting the terrain and their agility in dashing from cover to cover, exposing them as little as possible to enemy fire. In so far as their agility makes such tactics possible, the better the automotive performance of the tanks the higher, potentially, is their probability of survival. But the best automotive performance will make little difference if, instead of being based on fire and movement, the tactics of tanks amount to ponderous frontal assaults of the kind seen all too often in the past.

If a tank is hit, its probability of survival depends on its armour not being perforated, or otherwise disrupted, and, if perforated, on the damage not being lethal. Thus, the probability of survival can be expressed in terms of the probabilities of the events which contribute to it.

Given the probability of survival P_S in addition to the kill probability P_K, it is possible to calculate the probability P_{SE} that the tank will succeed in an engagement with an opposing tank, or some other weapon system. The simplest type of engagement is represented by the classical duel where the two opponents simultaneously fire at each other. In this case, P_{SE} is given by the expression

$$P_{SE} = P_K \times P_S$$
$$= P_K \times (1 - P_{K_0}) \quad (7.6)$$

A different situation exists in an engagement between two tanks where one fires before the other. In this case the probability that the tank which fires first will succeed is equal to the probability that it will kill the opposing tank multiplied not by the probability that it will survive when it is fired at (i.e. the probability that it will not be killed by the opposing tank) but by 1 minus the probability that it will be killed by the opposing tank multiplied by the probability that the opposing tank will survive the first shot, i.e.

$$P_{SE} = P_K \times [1 - P_{K_0} (1 - P_K)] \quad (7.7)$$

Clearly, the tank which fires first gains a very considerable advantage. Other things being equal, the tank which is likely to gain this advantage is the one with the simpler firing procedure and this generally means a simpler fire control system. The latter might well mean a lower hit and, therefore, kill probability but the ability to react more quickly might well outweigh this in many cases. A stationary tank in a defensive position is also more likely to gain this advantage than one which is moving and which is more likely to be spotted first. This, together with the much lower hit probability of a moving tank, gives tanks in defensive positions a very considerable advantage over those which attack, so much so that the attackers need to be four, or more, times as numerous as the defenders to have a chance of winning.

Equation (7.7) can be extended beyond the case of a single exchange of shots but even without doing this it is evident that if one tank has a significantly higher rate of fire than the other it might be able to fire a second shot before the other tank has reacted and thereby increase still further its chances of success. From this it is but a short step to the conclusion that the higher the rate of fire the higher is the probability of success.

The last major problem is that of the availability of tanks in time and space. If the employment of tanks were confined to set-piece battles, preceded by a slow build up of the opposing forces, which took place during both World Wars, the problem would hardly arise. But tank forces can not, as a rule, be prepositioned for battle, nor is their employment confined to short-range, head-on encounters. Instead, they have to move over varying distances and to manoeuvre, so that they can block or intercept each other, before they join battle. It is necessary therefore, to consider the probability that tanks will be available where and when they are wanted.

The concept of the availability of tanks in time and space is more meaningful than that of "mobility", which is usually invoked in this context and which is either too vague to be of use or is narrowly interpreted in terms of parameters such as maximum road speed. The probability that a tank will be available where and when it is wanted is not, unfortunately, easy to determine because of the complexity of the environment in which the tank operates. In essence, however, it amounts to the probability that the tank will cover a specified distance in a given time.

Apart from such obvious factors as a high average speed capability, the probability of covering a specified distance in a given time depends also on the probability of the tank being in running order, of being able to cross water obstacles unassisted or of finding bridges capable of supporting it, of being able to exploit other means of transportation, of not being stalled or at least considerably slowed down by soft ground when moving off the road, and so on.

Most of these probabilities are inversely related to the weight of tanks. In consequence, the heavier they are the lower is the probability that they will be available where and when they are needed. In the extreme, weight might completely negate the virtues of a tank. A good example of this is provided by the U.S. M6 heavy tank of the Second World War, which, in its day, possessed a very high kill probability and a high probability of survival. Yet its effectiveness was nil because it could not be made available where and when it was needed on account of its heavy weight,

Nevertheless, it is often argued that weight is of little consequence between about 15 tons, which represents the limit of air transportability, and 60 tons, or so, when the difficulties are too obvious to be ignored. Arguments of this kind fail to recognise the cumulative effect of weight increases, which makes the difficulties rise progressively with weight and not suddenly at 60 tons, or whatever might be the allegedly critical weight. For instance, the heavier the tank the higher, inevitably, is the minimum pressure which it exerts on the ground and the greater therefore, are the chances that it will get bogged down in difficult terrain. Thus, a 30-ton tank can have a nominal ground pressure of 10 lb/in^2 whereas a comparable 50 tonner will have 14 lb/in^2, which can cause it to stall in soft ground negotiable by the lighter vehicle.

Another facet of the availability of tanks in time and space which tends to be ignored is their reliability as vehicles. The problem is much the same as that of the reliability of tank armament, mentioned earlier, and it is obvious that a tank which is unreliable because of inadequate automotive development or which constitutes an unduly complex and vulnerable mechanism is far less likely to be available where and when it is needed than a simpler and more robust vehicle.

How harmful unreliability can be was demonstrated many times during the Second World War when tanks of all nationalities were kept out of battle or even had to be abandoned to the enemy because of failures of their automotive components. A much more recent example of unreliability was provided by the peace-time operation of the U.S. M48A2, which, according to a report of the Controller General of the U.S. Army, experienced on the average one major or minor breakdown per 36 miles of operation. No similar breakdown statistics have been published for other tanks but this is due to reticence on the part of the military authorities rather than the achievement of complete reliability, which remains a major problem with all tanks.

An almost unexplored approach towards greater reliability of tanks is by way of redundancy, which implies having additional components in parallel with those necessary to perform a given function. Systems incorporating such functionally redundant components are inevitably more complex, as well as more expensive, but, since the duplicated or triplicated components operate in parallel, their overall reliability is greater because they do not fail until all two, or three, components have failed. In consequence, systems which incorporate redundant components, or subsystems, are more reliable and this may well justify their increased cost or even weight. The larger the component the more difficult it is, of course, to duplicate it but the S-tank shows what can be done by having a twin-engine installation which enables either engine to drive it by itself. This does not provide complete duplication of power but, nevertheless, it greatly reduces the risk of the S-tank being immobilised through an engine failure. The S-tank also provides an example of the complete duplication of small subsystems as it has fully duplicated driving and fire controls.

The influence of availability on the overall probability of success may be indicated by comparing two hypothetical tanks X and Y, which have different probabilities of being available, of survival and of kill, when engaging a particular target.

Probability	*Tank*	
	X	*Y*
Kill probability, P_K	·50	·45
Probability of survival, P_S	·60	·50
Probability of being available, P_A	·40	·55
Probability of success, P_{SS}	·120	·124

As shown, tank X has a higher kill probability and a higher probability of survival. But, when the values of all three probabilities are substituted in equation (7.1), tank Y gives a higher probability of success P_{SS}, because it has a higher probability of being available in time and space. In general, tank X would also be the heavier of the two and since costs tend to be proportional to weight it would also be more expensive to produce. In consequence, not only would the lighter tank Y have a higher probability of success but it would be even better from the point of view of cost/effectiveness, that is of cost per successful mission which is the ultimate criterion in the evaluation of tank designs.

CHAPTER 8

Project Management

A STRIKING feature of the development of tanks since 1945 has been the length of time required in many cases to put new vehicles into service. The very first tanks went into action within thirteen months of the commencement of their design; during the Second World War the Tiger I still did it within 15 months and the U.S. M3 medium within 21 months. But, more recently, it took as much as nine years from the issue of the requirement for the Chieftain to its entry into service.

Suspicions that something might be wrong with the management of tank projects are usually exorcised with assurances that it is all part of the growing complexity of military equipment. Comforting beliefs of this kind lose their credibility, however, when it is realised that tanks such as the Chieftain are not all that much more complex than the Tiger and that other, no less sophisticated weapon systems have been put into operation in recent years in a fraction of the time claimed to be necessary for tanks. The most striking example of this is provided by the Polaris missile system which, for all its complexity, was put into operation by the U.S. Navy in four years from its inception, or about half the time taken by several contemporary tanks to reach a comparable stage of development.

The reasons for the long "lead" time from the inception of tank projects to the entry of vehicles into service and for other failings in tank development, are to be found in the processes by which tanks are developed. In general, the evolution of a new tank begins with a tentative operational requirement, a broad statement of the need for a particular type of vehicle which is formalised into what is known in Britain as a General Staff Target and in the United States as a Qualitative Material Development Objective. This is followed by a feasibility study through which the concept of the project assumes precision and is transformed into a General Staff Requirement or a Qualitative Material Requirement—a more detailed statement of the characteristics of the desired vehicle. The establishment of an operational requirement, and of the corresponding technical specification, is followed by a project study whose object is to examine more closely the implications of developing the desired vehicle, including the technical problems which will need to be resolved and costs, as well as the precise degree to which the requirement is likely to be met. Approval of the project is followed by detailed design and the construction of several prototypes. When ready, the prototypes are subjected to a programme of development tests and of user trials under operational conditions, on the completion of which an order is placed for the production of the vehicle.

On the face of it, the prevailing procedures appear eminently sound. But closer examination reveals several major weaknesses. The first shows up at the very beginning of the cycle of events and amounts to the fact that, under the system which prevails in Britain and elsewhere, most of the initiative in conceiving new equipment is expected to come from the service staffs who are responsible for formulating operational requirements. In theory a new operational requirement may, of course, be conceived anywhere. Moreover, service staffs generally formulate it with the assistance of technical advisers. But the fact remains that service staffs are still responsible for much of the synthesis of the military and technological factors into the broad conception of the new equipment and when the implications of this are considered they can hardly be regarded best fitted for it.

In general, the conception of a weapon or weapon system stems from considerations of what the military user does or may need and what is technically feasible. It combines the facts of the existing strategic and tactical situation, or deductions about possible or probable future conditions, with others drawn from the fund of scientific knowledge gained by research and from the existing technological capabilities, into a tentative technical solution to a military problem. Service staffs are, of course, well placed to assemble the strategic, tactical and intelligence ingredients. But they are not in intimate or continuous contact with technological problems. Yet they are expected to generate what is essentially a technical idea—a task for which they are obviously ill-fitted. In consequence, operational requirements are more likely to envisage improvements to existing equipment than original solutions. The service staff cannot be blamed for this, though they might have been more receptive to new ideas. The fault lies in the fact that they are badly mis-cast when they are expected to play the role of originators of new equipment.

Those who are concerned with project studies are, in principle, better fitted to take the initiative and to evolve ideas of really new equipment, which is, in fact, usually the consequence of inventive thinking at the design level. They live in a technical environment and are closer to the research which provides information and data necessary to devise new weapons or other equipment. However, this group also has its failings, even if they are less fundamental to conceiving new equipment. It commonly lacks breadth of outlook and sufficient knowledge of operational conditions to conceive what the user needs or, better still, anticipating his needs.

A way out of this difficulty is for the military authorities to foster suitably staffed technical study groups, which they would feed with the maximum of information and expect to synthesize the various factors into broad conceptions of new equipment. Ideally, two, or more, technical groups should work in competition with each other and be provided with strong incentives to have their ideas translated into operational equipment. The service staffs could then confine themselves to the proper executive functions of objective review and selection of proposals put to them by the technical groups, instead of having to take the initiative by writing operational requirements.

Something approaching this existed before the Second World War when Christie, Buckham, Carden and others pressed new ideas on service staffs in advance of the latter's requirements. The initiative of men of this stamp also eliminated the delays which arise between the inception of new projects and the establishment of technical specifications. In their absence much of the specifications is established by committees, with all that this implies in terms of diffuse responsibility and tenuous involvement in the success, or otherwise, of a particular project.

Committees are excellent, of course, for bringing together many different viewpoints and skills. But, in the nature of things, they lack the vision and initiative found in individuals. In consequence, the formulation of specifications is drawn out by arguments from various quarters, which can only be resolved quickly by the decisions of a forceful and sufficiently powerful individual determined to transform ideas into operation equipment.

Senior army officers concerned with the overall direction of tank development might be expected to take such decisions. But their stay in any particular post has been generally short and in Britain and the United States notoriously so. In consequence, they have usually had limited technical experience and this has inhibited them from taking a lead in technical matters. Or, if they attempted to take technical decisions in spite of it, their intervention was as likely to be harmful as beneficial.

The short tours of duty of senior officers in posts responsible for the overall direction of tank development have also tended to disrupt the continuity essential to the efficient management of projects. In its absence, there are greater chances of vacillations, of decisions being changed and, consequently, of delays both in the drawing up of requirements and of their transformation into operational equipment. The frequent changes in senior military posts have also removed much of the drive that comes from the personal involvement of those in executive positions in the progress of projects and from the knowledge of having to see a job through.

In the circumstances even more responsibility for the progress of projects devolves upon the engineers, who should, in any case, provide the lead in the transformation of ideas and research findings into usable equipment, since this field of activity is essentially theirs, as is much of the initiation of projects. However, the extent to which they lead varies according to their standing and the authority they wield. For instance, in France and Sweden, as well as the Soviet Union, the status of engineers is relatively high and they play a more prominent role in the development of projects than they do in Britain, where the standing of engineers is lower, to the detriment of the activities which depend on them. This is particularly true of government service within which much of the work on British military equipment is done. There, by tradition and recruitment policy, the Scientific Civil Service favours the research scientist and the analytical, research attitude to problems, even where other attributes might be more relevant. In consequence, there is a tendency within government establishments to pay more attention to analysing problems than to synthesising knowledge into useful equipment. Industry has an in-built corrective mechanism against any such imbalance between research activities and design engineering in its ultimate need to produce marketable products. This restores the importance of product engineering but its equivalent is absent from the workings of government services. The latter stand, therefore, in particular need of engineers able to uphold the importance of the design and development activities for which they are responsible, and to spur them on by effective technical leadership.

Another and not uncommon failing in the management of projects controlled by government agencies are the delays which occur during the transition from design and development to production. Except in emergencies, there is no stimulus of competition and government services clearly lack the incentives urging private industry to produce practical results. In consequence, full reign is given to the natural reluctance to commit oneself to the production of a particular design while the researchers and development engineers keep seeing further improvements.

The reluctance to commit oneself to the production of a particular design is evident enough in industrial organisations but the pressure of competition from other firms and the necessity of having saleable products for a firm to survive will eventually drive the most laggard management to a decision. Moreover, in industry there is also the lure of the timely decision bringing in direct reward. But in government service there are no equivalent whips or carrots with which decisions could be speeded up. Thus, the search for perfection, experimentation and re-design go on while the prospects of supplying new equipment to the users recede into the future. This can go to such lengths that when the first production units are finally made the original conception has largely outlived its usefulness and the newly-made equipment is already obsolescent. An extreme example of this is provided by the French type B tank, which was well conceived in the mid-twenties but which was obsolescent when it was first produced eleven years later.

To avoid such happenings and other, lesser, evils of protracted development, pressure must somehow be generated to initiate production of a particular design at the earliest possible time. Such pressure is, obviously, not likely to come from research scientists or even development engineers. It is much more likely to come from men with a broad experience of production but they are seldom to be found in government service, where research backgrounds predominate at decision making levels. This is almost as if major industrial organisation left production decisions to their research departments, which is difficult to imagine, however well qualified the research men might be in their specialist spheres of activity.

The most obvious advantage of an early start to production is the earlier deployment of new equipment. Admittedly equipment put into production at an early stage of its development will not have all the refinements it would have had were it produced later but it would be operational and far more useful to the user than promises of equipment which might be better but which has still to materialise. Other, less obvious but very important advantages are the earlier start to the development of manufacturing techniques, the feed-back of technical information based on far more realistic experience than that gained with a few especially made experimental models and the speeding-up of the development of new concepts, because of the release of effort from the refinement of earlier ones.

Decisions about going into production are easier to take when the evolution of tanks proceeds in a continuous series of small steps, when successive designs represent only a moderate advance on their predecessors and follow them relatively quickly, than when bigger jumps are attempted at longer intervals. In the first case the uncertainty about the outcome of decisions is less and there need be less hesitation, therefore, about taking them. They are also easier to implement, because the production facilities will require less development at any one time. Moreover, a relatively rapid succession of designs means less development work on any one and this can considerably advance the stage at which production begins.

How much time elapses before any decision to produce a particular model becomes effective depends to a very large extent on the amount of prior production planning and preparation. If little of it is done until most of the development testing is complete then a considerable amount of time is required to start production. On the other hand if production planning starts, as it can and should, at the project approval stage then a minimum of time is lost between the completion of development trials and the commencement of production. This again is more likely to occur when the evolution of tanks proceeds in a continuous series of small steps than in occasional big jumps. It is also more likely to occur under authoritarian regimes, where the necessary decisions are taken more readily.

Another cause of delays to the start of production planning is the concurrent design and development of more than one model. This has been done, among others, in the case of the Leopard, which started with two different designs and two different prototypes. One was produced by the MAK and Jung-Jungenthal companies and the other by the Rheinstahl Hanomag and Henschel companies and the decision which of the two would be adopted was only made after trials of the prototypes. More recently the same procedure has been adopted in the case of the U.S.-German MBT-70.

To the extent that it introduces an element of competition, the concurrent development of more than one design is bound to have a beneficial effect on the final product. But whether it is worth carrying it to the stage of competitive trials between prototypes is doubtful, as it prevents serious production planning until a choice has been made between the competing prototypes, as well as spreading the available resources between more than one project and to that extent slowing down design and development.

A well-managed tank project free of all such failings might follow a programme similar to that illustrated by the bar chart shown in Fig. xx. This shows the minimum duration of the principal activities from the inception of a project to the commencement of deliveries, divided into three groups which correspond to the three main phases of the programme: concept studies, design and development, and production. The last two are shown to overlap to a considerable extent: if they do not, it is readily seen how much longer a project programme can become.

The programme illustrated by the bar chart implies, among others, an adequate basis of research and component development from which to evolve designs. The existence of such a basis was responsible for much of the success of the tank development controlled by the U.S. Army Ordnance. In particular, it accounted for the fact that tanks such as the M3 medium could go into battle within 21 months of the issue of a requirement and yet prove far more reliable than other contemporary tanks with much longer development histories.

The duration of the feasibility and project studies could well be less than is indicated by the bar chart but it could also be considerably longer, particularly if a really radical departure from existing practices were involved or, what is much the same thing, if the work is started very largely from scratch. In any case they require relatively modest resources and are generally performed within government establishments, where the specialist knowledge and skills are largely concentrated. The British, French and United States examples of such establishments are, respectively, the Fighting Vehicles Research and Development Establishment at Chertsey, Surrey, the Atelier d'Issy-les-Moulineaux, at Satory near Versailles, and the U.S. Army-Tank Automotive Command, at Detroit Arsenal, Michigan.

The detail design, on the other hand, is almost invariably performed by industrial organisations with relevant experience and adequate draughting resources. This reduces the field to the larger automotive companies and armament firms which alone possess both. The magnitude of their task is indicated by the fact that even when fully developed major components, such as engines and transmissions, are available the

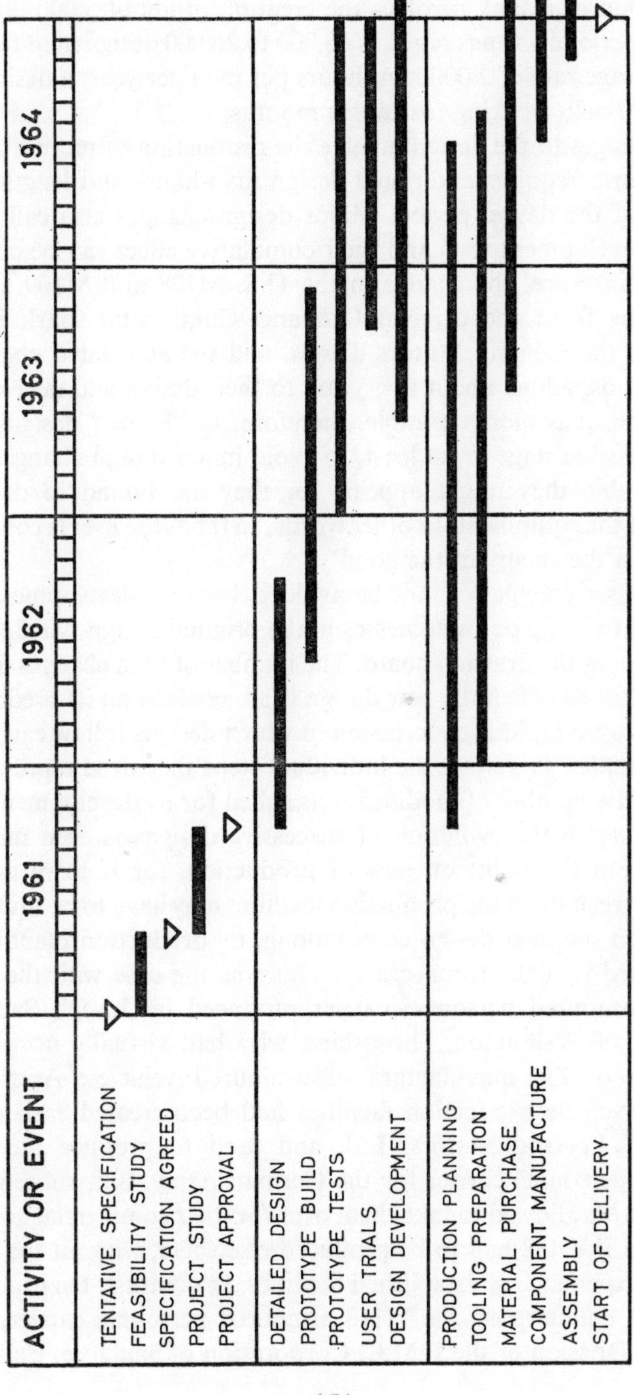

Fig. XX Bar chart of a tank project programme.

detail design of a tank involves the creation of about 5,000 drawings. This number of drawings requires 65,000 to 75,000 design man-hours or, at the average rate of 2,000 man-hours per man per year, a design team of 30 to 40 men working for twelve months.

Any changes to the design involve the production of more drawings. This, in turn, requires additional design man-hours and lengthens the duration of the design period. Major design changes also call for additional development tests and their cumulative effect can be considerable. For instance, the change in the U.S. M108 and M109 self-propelled guns from the original Ordnance-Continental spark ignition engines to the General Motors diesels, and the associated changes in transmissions, added about two years to their design and development programme. It is most desirable, therefore, to "freeze" designs at the earliest possible stage or, at least, to avoid major design changes, however desirable they might appear, for they are bound to delay the delivery of the equipment. In other words, so far as the user is concerned, the "best is the enemy of the good".

Some lesser changes cannot be avoided because development trials are bound to bring out weaknesses in the original design which cannot be foreseen on the drawing board. The number of such changes depends on the extent to which the new design is an advance on its predecessor. Thus, the more rapid the succession in which designs follow each other, and the smaller, therefore, the individual steps they need represent, the smaller is the number of modifications called for by development trials.

Continuity in the evolution of successive designs is even more important from the point of view of production, for if there are long breaks between them the production facilities may have to be shut down. Then, when the next design comes along, its production planning has to be started virtually from scratch. This was the case with the British F.V.432 armoured personnel carrier produced by Joseph Sankey & Co., Ltd., of Wellington, Shropshire, who had virtually no previous experience of the manufacture of armoured vehicles. Appropriate armoured vehicle production facilities had been created earlier as an adjunct of Leyland Motors, Ltd. and used to produce the HS.30 armoured personnel carrier for the German Army. But, subsequently, Leylands were allowed to take them over for their commercial activities, so that the F.V.432 had to be produced elsewhere, without the benefit of earlier experience or established facilities. In contrast, the production of its U.S. counterpart, the M113 armoured personnel carrier, by the Ordnance Division of the F.M.C. Corporation of San Jose, California, followed closely on that of the M59 carrier which, in turn, followed that of the M75. In consequence, the M113 enjoyed all the advantages which accrue from accumulated experience and well-established facilities, with the inevitable result that it was produced much more quickly than the F.V.432. In fact, the M113 began to be delivered from production only 3 years and 8 months after the award to F.M.C. of the initial development contract whereas the F.V.432 required more than six years to reach a comparable stage of development.

Even when the production of one design follows on that of another it is a considerable undertaking. It involves detail planning of numerous processes and facilities, purchase of additional or new production equipment, and the purchase of materials and parts, as well as the actual operation of production plants. The magnitude of the problem is indicated by the fact that a contemporary tank consists of about 30,000 different parts, or 100,000 pieces—when every nut and bolt is counted separately. This is about six times the number of pieces in an average motor car and it may involve as many as 2,000 different suppliers.

The production of tanks is, evidently, a complex undertaking which requires close coordination of numerous activities and the preparation for which must be started at the earliest possible stage if excessive delays in the delivery of new equipment are to be avoided. An early start to production planning means that modifications will have to be made to production equipment and schedules as a result of design changes called for by development trials but this is a price well worth paying for the much earlier delivery of new vehicles.

The interrelationship between the different activities is illustrated by the network diagram shown in Fig. XXI. Diagrams of this kind have come into use since the value of network analysis was demonstrated by the Program Evaluation and Review Technique, or PERT, devised in 1958 by the Bureau of Ordnance of the U.S. Navy for scheduling and controlling the Polaris missile project. In essence, PERT and other network analysis techniques involve the breaking down of projects into a set of activities or events and arranging them into a logical network. The durations of the activities are then estimated and added along different network paths between the start of a project and its completion to identify the longest, which gives the shortest total project time and which is, clearly, the critical path. Network analysis leads therefore, to a more rigorous examination of projects, to more realistic project time estimates and to the identification of the critical sequence of activities

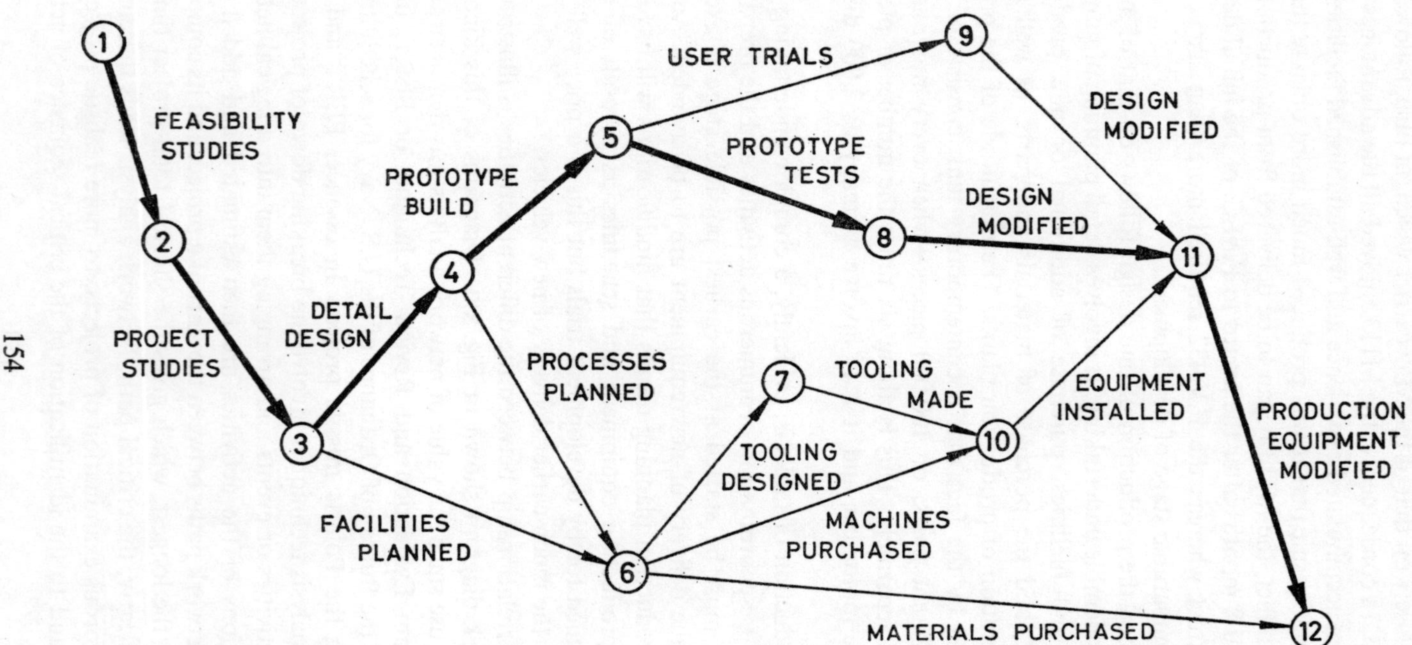

Fig. XXI Network diagram for a tank project with the critical path shown by heavy arrows.

on which attention needs to be concentrated if total project time is to be shortened.

The network diagram shown in Fig. XXI represents a greatly simplified result of the application of such analysis to a tank project. The activities which make up the project are represented by arrows: their lengths have no significance since the diagram defines only the sequence and interrelationships between the activities. The beginning and end of each activity are events which are represented by numbered circles, called nodes. Thus, node 1 represents the inception of the project, node 2 the operational requirement being agreed, node 3 project approval and node 12 the commencement of production.

The critical path for the network illustrated is most likely to run through nodes 1–2–3–4–5–8–11–12, as indicated by the heavy arrows. Other arrangements of activities would give a different critical path. For instance, if process planning were only started after the completion of prototype trials and the resulting design modifications the critical path would be very much longer.

Of the activities which make up the critical path in the optimised network illustrated in Fig. XXI, the most time-consuming, generally, is 5–8, the prototype testing and development. It requires, therefore, particularly close control. Its duration, like that of other activities, can be shortened by the allocation of additional resources but the cost of doing this may be high and time cannot be saved regardless of expense. In consequence, project management has to cover cost as well as time control.

CHAPTER 9

Tracked Armoured Personnel Carriers

TRACKED armoured personnel carriers are a relatively new type of vehicle, whose employment is very much more recent than that of tanks and indeed most other items of military equipment. This is remarkable in view of the fact that the first tracked armoured carrier was designed in Britain in 1917. Moreover, thirty-five vehicles of this type, called the Mark IX, were built in 1918. But nothing more was done about tracked armoured personnel carriers for twenty-five years.

In fact, it was only after the Second World War that the development of tracked armoured personnel carriers was taken up in earnest and it was only during the late fifties that they began to be used on a large scale.

The reasons for this remarkable delay in the development of tracked armoured carriers lie principally in a lack of appreciation of the value of mechanised infantry. Thus, even the most ardent advocates of mechanisation failed to recognise its value and generally confined their attention to tanks, which they mistakenly regarded as self-sufficient.

It was only during the late thirties that the German Army first established the need to include in mechanised, or armoured, formations an effective infantry component, as well as tanks. To be effective the infantry component of armoured formations had to be able to work closely with tanks and this meant providing it with comparable battlefield mobility. In consequence, by 1940, the infantry units of the Panzer divisions began to be equipped with half-track armoured personnel carriers, in place of trucks (Pl. 112). The U.S. Army followed suit and between 1941 and 1945 produced 41,000 armoured half-track carriers, mainly for use by the infantry of its own and allied armoured divisions (Pl. 113).

The German and American half-tracks of the Second World War represented a considerable advance on the earlier method of transporting infantry in trucks but they left a good deal to be desired, both from the point of view of protection and cross-country mobility. As a result, attempts were made in 1944 by British and Canadian units in

Normandy to devise better vehicles by converting M4 Sherman and Ram medium tanks and M7 105 mm self-propelled howitzers into infantry carriers. These improvised carriers were given the generic name of Kangaroos and, in spite of their makeshift nature, were used with some success in the final stages of the war in Europe.

At about the same time the U.S. Army started to develop similar vehicles and these led to the first of the post-war generation of tracked armoured personnel carriers. The first of the fully tracked carriers built in the United States, in 1943–1944, was the T41, later M39, Armoured Utility Vehicle. This was essentially an M18 tank destroyer without its 76 mm gun turret and with a slightly raised superstructure. It was similar, therefore, to the improvised Kangaroo carriers and suffered from the shortcomings inherent in this type of vehicle. In particular, it offered no overhead protection to its occupants who, moreover, had to dismount by jumping over the side, which exposed them unnecessarily to enemy fire and to the risk of injury due to a bad fall with full equipment.

A remedy for both major shortcomings of the M39 was found in 1945, in the development of the M44 Armoured Utility Vehicle (Pl. 114). This too was based on the chassis of the M18 tank destroyer but modified almost beyond recognition. Its most striking feature was an enclosed box-like armoured body at the rear of which there were access doors, made possible by relocating the engine at the front.

To the extent that it afforded overhead protection to its occupants and no longer required them to jump over the side, the M44 Armoured Utility Vehicle represented a very considerable advance on the earlier M39. It was, however, large and cumbersome, being capable of carrying as many as 27 men. This made it present a large target and was out of keeping with the usual tactical division of the infantry into squads or sections of ten to twelve men. As a result, only a few M44 were built. They did, however, serve to demonstrate the potential advantages of fully enclosed tracked armoured carriers and thus helped the acceptance of this type of vehicle by the U.S. Army. Moreover, they set the pattern for much of the subsequent development of carriers, not only in the United States but elsewhere.

The T18 which followed the M44 was, in fact, little more than a scaled-down version of the latter. It had the same kind of simple box body with two rear doors but, because it carried 12 instead of 27 men, it was smaller and lighter. It differed also in incorporating many mechanical components of the contemporary T41 light tank.

By the time the T18 prototype was built in 1948, the U.S. Army had already decided to equip the infantry units of its armoured divisions with tracked armoured personnel carriers instead of the earlier half-tracks. Troop trials in 1951 only confirmed that decision and a slightly modified version of the T18 was ordered from the International Harvester Company. The production model became known as the M75 Armoured Personnel Carrier and came into service with the armoured formations by 1953. (Pl. 115).

In the meantime, the outbreak of the war in Korea in 1950, gave further impetus to the development of armoured personnel carriers. In 1953 a few M75, as well as M39, were used by the U.S. Army in Korea and showed that they could be of considerable value to infantry formations, as well as being essential to the infantry units of the armoured divisions. Still greater impetus to the development was given by the tests with tactical nuclear weapons in Nevada, in 1955. These tests demonstrated that armoured personnel carriers enabled the infantry to operate in relative proximity to nuclear explosions and raised the demand for the provision of armoured carriers to infantry, as well as armoured, divisions. At that time the U.S. Army is believed to have already had 3,600 carriers in use or on order but subsequent orders increased their number very considerably.

The armoured personnel carriers which took such a successful part in the 1955 nuclear tests were of the then newly produced M59 type. The origins of this vehicle went back to a 1950 U.S. Army requirement for an improved model to succeed the M75, which led the Ordnance Division of the Food Machinery and Chemical, or F.M.C., Corporation to design a vehicle similar to the M75 and yet superior to it in several respects (Fig. XXII and Pl. 116).

The F.M.C. Corporation had already played a leading role in the development of LVTs, as well as sharing in the production of the M75, and its experience with amphibious vehicles led to the development of the M59 Armoured Infantry Vehicle as an amphibian. This was not too difficult to achieve from the basis of the M75 in view of its bulk, which provided sufficient buoyancy for flotation. The main problem, apart from the water-proofing of the hull, was to devise a bow configuration appropriate to operation in water without, at the same time, compromising the characteristics of the vehicle on land.

The solution to this problem was found in a trim vane hinged on the lower part of the hull front and rotated forward for operation in water. Propulsion in water presented no basic problem. It had already been

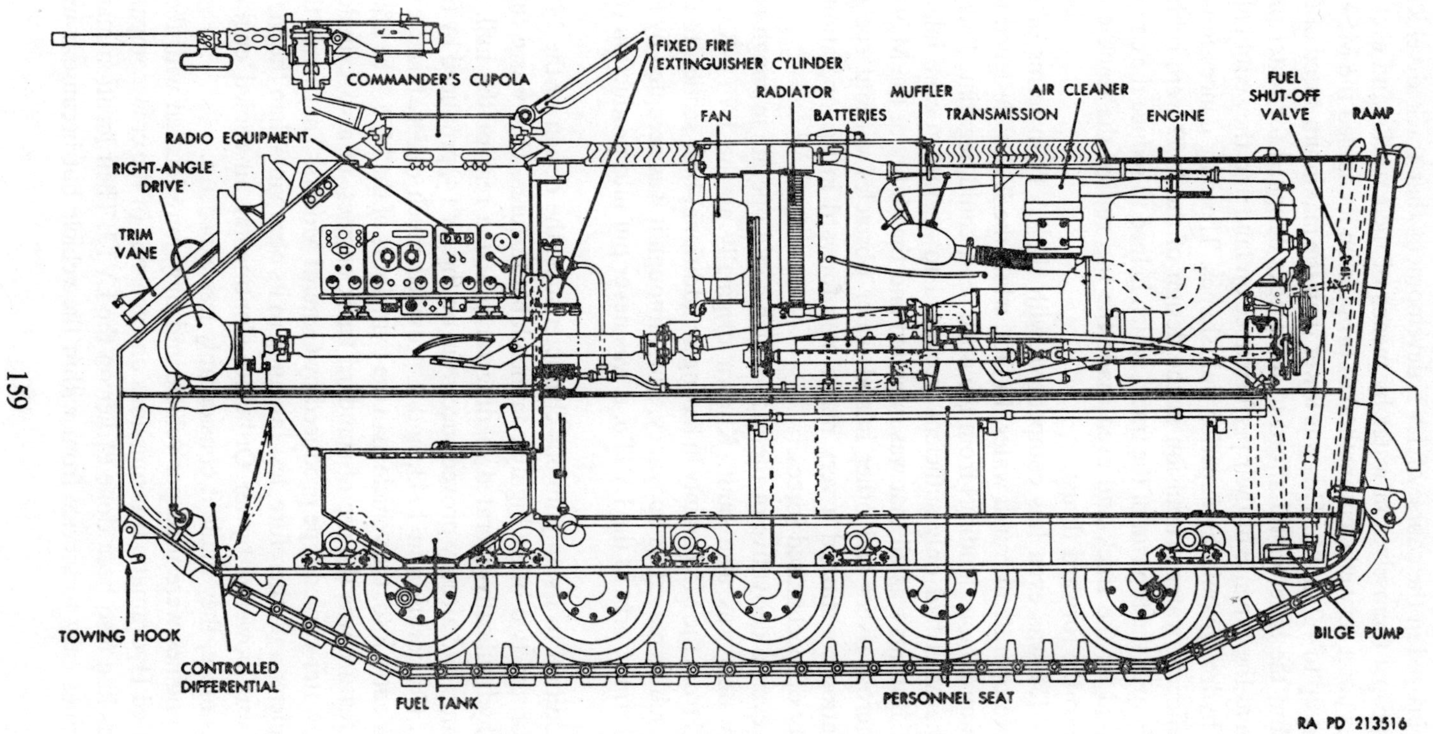

Fig. XXII Cross section of the U.S. M59 Armoured Infantry Vehicle.

amply proved in the course of LVT development that tracked vehicles could propel themselves in water by means of their tracks and even if this was not a very efficient method of propulsion it enabled the M59 to swim at up to 4·2 m.p.h. This was lower than the maximum speed of the LVTs but the latter could afford to use tracks designed for water propulsion at the expense of their performance on land and they could also afford hydrodynamically superior hull shapes. The only concession to more efficient water propulsion in the design of the M59 were rubber shrouds over the top run of the track, which helped to reduce the energy dissipated by the track and even made the top run of the track contribute to the forward thrust.

The M59 was even less competitive with the LVTs in terms of its ability to operate in rough water. In fact, while the LVTs, designed for use in amphibious landings from the open seas, could negotiate Pacific surf, the M59 had only sufficient freeboard to operate in calm inland waters. But this was all that was intended and the ability of the M59 to swim across rivers and other inland water obstacles without special preparation constituted a very major step forward in the operational mobility of mechanised forces.

However, a derivative of the M59 which could operate in rough offshore waters was also built. Known originally as the LVTP-X2, it differed from the M59 mainly in having an additional bow section to the hull which increased its buoyancy. But, although it was accepted by the U.S. Marine Corps as the LVTP6, it was never put into production (Pl. 117).

In addition to its amphibious characteristics, the design of the M59 incorporated two other highly commendable features. One was a full-width hydraulically-operated loading ramp at the rear of the hull. A stern ramp had already proved successful on the LVT4, produced by the F.M.C. Corporation in 1943, and it provided much easier, faster exit from,or entry into, the vehicle than the twin doors of the M75. The other design feature was the use of standard truck engines, of a six-cylinder, in-line, water-cooled type produced by General Motors. They made the M59 quieter and, therefore, less fatiguing to its occupants than the M75, which was powered by an Ordnance-Continental air-cooled engine. What is more, they made it considerably less expensive.

Two engines were used per vehicle and they were located with their associated Hydramatic transmissions on each side of the crew compartment, as had also been done earlier on the LVT3. Their location made the engines easy to service from within the vehicle but because it was fairly high—above the tracks—it raised appreciably the centre of gravity of the vehicle. However, the most important point about the engines of the M59 was the contribution they made to reducing its cost. The cost of its predecessor, the M75, was variously quoted at the time at between 89,000 and 132,000 dollars, while that of the M59 was only 28,000 dollars, which was most important in view of the growing demand for armoured personnel carriers.

The first production order for the M59 was placed at the end of 1952, and deliveries to the troops began as early as the spring of 1954. In fact, the total time which elapsed from the issue of the U.S. Army requirement to the equipping of the first armoured infantry battalion with its 85 M59 carriers was only 3 years and 4 months. This notably short time shows what can be done given a sense of urgency together with an adequate background of earlier developments and established production facilities. By the same token, the history of the M59 demolishes complacent arguments that the development of this type of equipment requires six, or more, years.

Production of the M59 continued at the San Jose, California, plant of the F.M.C. Corporation until 1960, when its place was taken over by the current M113 Armoured Personnel Carrier (Pl. 118). The M113 is essentially a direct development of the M59, but it differs in several important respects, including aluminium alloy armour.

The M113 is actually the first aluminium armoured vehicle ever to have been put into production. When its development began in mid-1956, there was still an almost identical steel-armoured T117 model in addition to the aluminium armoured T113. Although the T113 was ultimately adopted, there was little to choose between it and the T117 so far as weight was concerned, because the areal density of aluminium armour is virtually the same as that of steel armour for any given degree of ballistic protection. Thus, aluminium armour 1·25 in thick had to be used to provide the same degree of protection as the $\frac{3}{8}$ in steel armour plate commonly used in the construction of the earlier carriers, and the weight of the two hulls was much the same. However, aluminium armour was easier to weld and the thicker aluminium plates made the hull structure more rigid, so that the T113 could dispense with some of the structural stiffeners needed by the T117.

What was more important than the 6 per cent weight difference between the T113 and T117 was that both were very considerably lighter than the M59. In fact, the M113 weighed 23,520 lb fully laden and only 18,410 lb when prepared for dropping by parachute. It says a great deal for the optimism of the military planners that they ever contemplated a significant number of armoured carriers being carried into action by air but their emphasis on air-transportability, and therefore on light weight, has had a very beneficial influence on the overall mobility of the M113.

The lighter weight of the M113 has gone hand in hand with a commendably lower silhouette and a redesigned track layout. In contrast to all the earlier U.S. carriers, the M113 dispensed with track return rollers. Thus, as in the Christie-type suspensions, the track runs back over the top of the road wheels and the weight of the return rollers is saved. The track itself is similar to that of the earlier U.S. carriers, having rubber-bushed single-pin links with detachable rubber road pads but altered in detail and made more durable. Its life commonly exceeds the 3,000-mile target originally laid down and in some cases has even attained 9,000 miles.

Otherwise, the principal characteristics of the M113 are much the same as those of the M59. It has similar amphibious capabilities, which enable it to cross inland waterways without preparation, and it can propel itself in water at up to 3·7 m.p.h. (Pl. 119). Like the M59 it has a hydraulically-operated rear ramp and it is powered by a commercial type engine located at the front, by the side of the driver (Pl. 120). In the original M113 vehicles the engine is a militarised version of a 361 in^3 Chrysler V-8 spark ignition engine, while the M113A1 produced since 1964 is powered by a General Motors V-6 two-stroke diesel.

The use of commercial engines has helped to make the M113 even less expensive than the M59. In fact, without radio and armament, it costs only 22,000 dollars, or £8,000, which is remarkably low compared with the cost of any other contemporary armoured vehicle.

The low cost combined with its other features has led to large orders for the M113 not only from the U.S. Army but also from several others. The first U.S. Army production order, for 900 vehicles, was given in mid-1959, and it is noteworthy that delivery commenced within a year, or only 3 years and 8 months after the award of the initial development contract. The combination of quick delivery with low cost helped the F.M.C. Corporation to secure an order in 1962 from the German Army for 1,132 to supplement its other carriers and low cost also had an important bearing on a 1963 Swiss Army order for 800 carriers, which became known in Switzerland as the Spz. 63. Cost also influenced the decision taken in 1963 by the Canadian Army to abandon its own Bobcat carrier in favour of the M113.

Several other countries have also adopted the M113, including Australia, Italy and the Netherlands, as well as Denmark, Spain, Greece, Turkey, Iran, Pakistan, Thailand, Viet Nam and Korea. Moreover, not only was the M113 produced in the United States, at the San Jose, California, and Charleston, West Virginia, plants of the F.M.C. Corporation but also in Italy, by OTO Melara SpA, of La Spezia, as a result of a "co-production" agreement signed in 1963 by the United States and Italian Governments. In consequence, more than 26,000 M113 carriers and their derivatives were produced by the autumn of 1966, and they became the most widely used armoured vehicles outside the Soviet bloc.

Successful as it is, the design of the M113 armoured carrier is not beyond criticism. Although its silhouette is much lower than that of the earlier M75 and M59 carriers, its box-like superstructure with vertical side plates leaves much to be desired ballistically. Another and far more serious criticism of the M113 is the inability of its occupants to fight from within it. This fault stems from the tactical doctrine adopted by the U.S. Army that infantry must dismount to close with the enemy and by the same token that it was not expected to fight from its carriers. In consequence, the United States carriers have been designed as transport rather than fighting vehicles, in striking contrast to the methods successfully evolved during the Second World War by the German Panzer Grenadiers of fighting, whenever possible, from their carriers, on the move. To put it more picturesquely, the U.S. Army concept of the armoured personnel carrier has been merely that of a "battle taxi".

Like its predecessors, the M113 is, of course, fitted with an externally mounted ·5 in machine gun. But to fire it the gunner has to expose himself and it was only as a result of experience with M113 carriers in Viet Nam, where the casualties among the gunners were inevitably high, that improvised protection was fitted around the ·5 in machine gun (Pl. 121). Most other occupants of the M113 sit on benches facing inwards, as in the M75 and M59, and are unable to fire their weapons or even to observe what goes on outside (Pl. 122). As a result not only are they mere passengers while they remain in the carrier but when, eventually, they come to dismount for action they have little idea of the situation in which they find themselves.

The same criticisms apply to the British FV.432 armoured personnel carrier, which is, in effect, a copy of the M113. The development of the FV.432 was preceded by that of the Bren Gun Carrier, which was produced on a large scale during the Second World War but which was only intended for the limited role of transporting three- or four-man light machine gun or reconnaissance teams. The Bren Gun Carrier was not big enough, therefore, to act as an armoured personnel carrier in the full sense of the word. The same applied to the somewhat larger but generally similar Universal Carriers, which were intended for towing infantry anti-tank guns and similar purposes. But in 1946, a new Universal Carrier was specified, the FV.401 Cambridge, which might have become the first tracked armoured personnel carrier of the British Army (Pl. 123).

As built in prototype form in 1950, the FV.401 represented a considerable advance on the earlier Universal Carriers. It was powered by a Rolls-Royce B.80 8-cylinder engine, had a Wilson-type epicyclic transmission and an independent torsion bar suspension. What is more, it could carry seven men. This was low by contemporary standards but would have been sufficient for the FV. 401 to act as a personnel carrier. Its general layout was no better than that of carriers improvised from tanks but if the crew still had to jump over the top because of the rear engine location their compartment was at least provided with hinged covers. Moreover, the FV.401 carried a collapsible flotation screen which, when erected, provided sufficient buoyancy for swimmig across water obstacles.

However, the FV.401 was never put into production. At the time the British General Staff still failed to recognise the need for tracked armoured personnel carriers, due largely to a continued lack of appreciation of the importance of combining tanks with a strong and closely integrated armoured infantry component, a lack which bedevilled the evolution of British armoured formations since the twenties. As a result, orders were placed for the Alvis Saracen wheeled armoured carrier—an excellent vehicle in many ways but more suited to rushing small bodies of riflemen from one part of the battlefield to the other than to close and sustained cooperation with tanks. Moreover, only a relatively small number of infantry battalions was equipped with Saracens, partly because of their cost but even more because a higher proportion of armoured infantry was not considered necessary.

It was only in 1958 that the War Office issued a requirement for a tracked carrier, the FV.432 (Pl. 124). Then four more years had to pass before an order was placed, in 1962, with Joseph Sankey and Sons Ltd., of Wellington, Shropshire, for the production of 1,000 vehicles. Within that length of time several other carriers have been developed to the stage of being in service. Yet the design of the FV.432 was not very original, following as it did that of the M113.

Thus, the FV.432 has the same box-like hull as the M113 and a similar independent torsion bar suspension with rubber-bushed, single-pin tracks with detachable rubber road pads. It does not, however, have a rear ramp but a single large door and the top run of the track is supported by return rollers, as on the earlier U.S. carriers. It also has a larger, circular hatch over the crew compartment and the engine is on the left of the driver, instead of being on the right. The engine itself is a Rolls-Royce K.60 diesel but early production models were still powered by a Rolls-Royce B.81 spark ignition engine.

Unlike the M113, the FV.432 has a steel hull but what is far more important is that it is 4 tons heavier, without having significantly greater overall dimensions. In consequence, it does not have sufficient buoyancy to cross water obstacles unaided. To overcome this a collapsible flotation screen has been resorted to once again (Pl. 125). This not only provides sufficient freeboard for operation in calm inland waters but enables the FV.432 to paddle itself ashore from landing craft in relatively choppy seas. But the flotation screen takes time to erect and is vulnerable to damage. Moreover, it adds to the high cost of the FV.432, which is more than twice that of the M113.

In the meantime, while the British Army was copying the U.S. M113, the French Army produced an original design which represented the first attempt at a tracked armoured carrier that was not merely a 'battle taxi" but a vehicle from which the infantry could fight on the move. The vehicle was the AMX-VTT, or *Véhicule Transport de Troupe*, which was designed to a requirement issued by the French Army in 1954 (Pl. 126). Two years later prototypes were already available for user trials and production models began to be delivered in 1958. Since then the AMX-VTT has become the standard armoured personnel carrier of the French Army and it has also been purchased by the Netherlands Army as well as being adopted in Belgium where several hundred were built under a joint Franco-Belgian production scheme.

Mechanically the AMX-VTT is based on the AMX 13 light tank. It is, in fact, one of a rationalised series of 17 light armoured vehicles based on the AMX 13 chassis. As such it enjoys several logistical advantages but the rationalisation with other vehicles restricted the freedom of action of its designers. This is particularly evident in the retention, almost unchanged, of the front section of the AMX 13 hull with its side-by-side engine and driving compartments. As a result, the front end of the AMX-VTT is not as good as it might be both from the point of view of compactness and of ballistic protection. But, on the credit side, the AMX-VTT has a turret with a 7·5 mm machine gun and other weapons can also be fired through openings in the sides of the superstructure, the crew seats being arranged to face outwards for this purpose (Pl. 127).

An even greater contrast to the type of armoured carrier developed in the United States is provided by the HS-30 carrier of the German Army (Pl. 128). Its Panzer Grenadiers pioneered fighting from armoured carriers and it demanded for them something better than a mere "battle taxi"—a combat carrier, in fact. As a result, the HS-30 has a very much lower silhouette than the U.S.-type of carrier. Its hull is also ballistically far better shaped and made of thicker plates. The frontal plate is, in fact, 30 mm thick and inclined at 55 degrees to the vertical and the superstructure side plates are 15 mm thick and inclined at 35 degrees. In consequence, its front is immune to 20 mm automatic gun projectiles and its sides to ·5 in heavy machine gun ammunition whereas the $\frac{3}{8}$ in (9·5 mm) vertical plates typical of the earlier U.S. carriers provided protection only against rifle-calibre ball ammunition and shell splinters. What is more, the HS-30 is armed with a turret-mounted, high velocity Hispano Suiza 820L 20 mm automatic gun whose adoption represented a major step forward in the offensive armament of armoured carriers.

For all its commendable features, the design of the HS-30 still leaves some things to be desired. In particular, its crew still have to jump over the side to dismount, because of the location of the engine compartment at the rear. Its crew are also unable to observe or fire with weapons other than the 20 mm gun without exposing themselves out of the roof openings (Pl. 129).

The shortcomings of the HS-30 are due partly to it being based on a chassis developed for other purposes, namely for an experimental twin 30 mm gun anti-aircraft gun developed as a private venture by the Hispano Suiza (Suisse) S.A., of Geneva. Coupled with this was the fact that the design of the HS-30 was evolved at a time when the German Army was being re-created, after almost ten years of demilitarisation of Germany, and wanted armoured carriers urgently, as it attached considerable importance to equipping its infantry with them, in spite of the scorn which many people in Britain and elsewhere poured at the time on the idea. In consequence, the design of the HS-30 was not developed as fully as it might have been.

The initial development contract for the HS-30 was awarded to

Hispano Suiza in 1956 and testing of the prototypes started in 1957. Production orders were placed a year later but, since the parent company had no facilities for the large scale production of vehicles, they were divided, for political reasons, between Leyland Motors Ltd. in Britain and the Henschel and Hanomag companies in Germany. The orders originally called for 3,600 carriers, at about £20,000 each, but the total was subsequently reduced to about 2,000. Production deliveries commenced in 1960 and the HS-30 has since been given the designation SPz 12-3.

At least one major shortcoming of the HS-30 was eliminated in the 4K carrier developed at the same time by the Oesterreichische Saurer-Werke AG, of Vienna. The design of the Saurer carrier stemmed from a requirement issued in 1956 by the Austrian Army which, like the German, called for a combat carrier. This led to a low silhouette vehicle with a ballistically well shaped hull but having the engine more sensibly located at the front. Thus, in contrast to the HS-30, the Saurer carrier has doors at the rear of the hull which allow its crew to dismount without jumping over the top. The 4K carrier has not been provided with the 20 mm gun turret which it was originally intended to have and the first vehicles delivered to the Austrian Army in 1959 did not even have overhead protection for the crew compartment but this has been put right since (Pls. 130 and 131).

In addition to being produced for the Austrian Army, the Saurer carrier also served as the basis of an experimental carrier built in 1958 in Switzerland by AG Adolph Saurer, of Arbon. Called the Tartaruga, this experimental vehicle was essentially a lengthened version of the Austrian carrier with a turret-mounted 20 mm Oerlikon gun (Pl. 132). It was built to a Swiss Army requirement but it never advanced beyond the prototype stage.

Another carrier built to the same Swiss Army requirement by the Mowag Motorwagenfabrik AG, of Kreuzlingen, was not only constructed in prototype form in 1957, but was evaluated in 1958 in Italy and in 1959 in Germany. However, it was never put into production and its place has been taken by a much improved model, also called the Pirate (Pl. 133). Like the HS-30, the new Mowag Pirate has a low, well-shaped hull with frontal armour thick enough to resist 20 mm gun projectiles and a turret-mounted 20 mm Oerlikon automatic gun. It is larger and heavier, however, being designed to carry 12, instead of 8, men and it has double rear doors so that the crew do not have to jump over the top. To provide rear access to the crew compartment the engine has had to be moved forward but instead of being located at the front, alongside the driver, as it was in the original version of the Pirate, as well as the two Saurer carriers, the new Pirate has it in the centre, with the turret ahead of it. In consequence, the turret is well forward, only just behind the driver and the commander who sit on either side of the vehicle. At the same time, there is direct communication between the commander's and driver's stations and the rest of the crew who are located on either side of the central engine compartment and behind it. All this amounts to an arrangement superior to that of any earlier carrier. The new Pirate has still not been provided with firing ports in the sides of the hull superstructure but, in addition to the 20 mm gun, the crew can fire light machine guns without exposing themselves as there is one machine gun mounting on each side of the superstructure operated by remote control from within the crew compartment.

Yet another arrangement is represented by the Japanese SU Type 60 carrier (Pl. 134). This has a six-man crew compartment at the rear of the hull while the centre is occupied by the engine compartment and, alongside it on the right, the gunner of an externally mounted ·5 in machine gun. At the front, in addition to the driver, there is a gunner who operates a 7·7 mm machine gun mounted in the frontal plate; behind them, in the centre, is the commander. Thus at least one weapon can be fired without the crew exposing themselves but otherwise the layout of the Type 60 carrier has little to commend it, except for its low silhouette. But the low silhouette also means that it cannot be an amphibian, in spite of a superficial resemblance to the U.S. M59 and M113 carriers.

The most commendable thing about the Japanese Type 60 is the speed with which it was developed. Work on it began in 1956 and, in spite of a major redesign after the testing of the first prototype in 1958, the first production vehicle was delivered from the Tokyo Motor Vehicle Works of Mitsubishi Nippon Heavy Industries Ltd., in 1960, 3 years and 11 months after the work began. This was particularly remarkable in view of the complete break in the Japanese development of armoured vehicles caused by the demilitarisation of Japan in 1945.

The reduction in the size of the target offered by a carrier which can be achieved at the expense of its amphibious characteristics and which has been illustrated by the Japanese Type 60 has been shown even more clearly by the German HW-K 11 (Pl. 135). This was developed by the Rheinstahl Henschel AG, of Kassel, using the same Chrysler engine and

Allison transmission as the U.S. M113 carrier. But, because it was not intended to float, it is 2 ft lower than the American carrier. Moreover, it has a ballistically better shaped hull.

The HW-K 11 was developed as a private venture and only a small number of it was produced, for the Mexican Army, which acquired the first few in 1964. An entirely different vehicle has been developed in the meantime by the associated Rheinstahl Hanomag company, of Hannover, working to a German Army requirement for a successor to the HS-30, or SPz 12-3. The *Schützenpanzer-neu*, as it is called, shares with the HW K-11 the basic idea that it should be a combat carrier with a low silhouette and a hull with well-sloped plates. Its actual layout, however is more like that of the Saurer 4K3F carrier, except that it has a 20 mm gun turret, and its chassis design is basically the same as that of the *Jagdpanzer* (*Kanone*) with which it forms part of a rationalised series of tracked armoured vehicles of between 17 and 25 tons.

In contrast to the heavier *Jagdpanzer*, the Spz (neu) is powered by a V-6 MB 833, instead of a V-8, model of the Daimler Benz series of compression ignition engines based on a common cylinder size. Moreover, the engine compartment is at the front, to allow for a crew compartment at the rear. The crew consists of ten men, including the driver and the turret gunner. Prototypes of the Spz (neu) still lacked firing ports in the sides of the superstructure but this has since been put right and the turret mounting has been very sensibly developed to take a rifle-calibre machine gun in addition to the 20 mm Hispano Suiza gun.

The Spz (neu) is greatly superior to the M113 as a combat vehicle but, inevitably, it lacks the inherent buoyancy of the latter. It cannot, therefore, swim across water obstacles, unless fitted with a collapsible flotation screen, or some similar device. But the flotation screen would have added to its weight, as well as being very vulnerable to enemy fire, and the idea of using it was rejected. Instead, the Spz (neu) has been designed to ford submerged, to a depth of up to 16 ft, using a schnorkel tube similar to that of the Russian T-54 and adopted earlier for the *Jagdpanzer* (*Kanone*).

The Swedish Army, on the other hand, has tried to combine the amphibious characteristics of the M113 type of carrier with the fighting capabilities of the combat carrier. However, its first step in the development of tracked armoured personnel carriers was the conversion of a number of Strv m/41 light tanks into Pbv 301 carriers (Pl. 136). These are the most successful of all the carriers converted from tanks, because the tank on which the conversion was based was mechanically one of the best tracked vehicles produced during the Second World War and because it was done thoroughly. It involved moving the engine compartment forward, raising the superstructure to create a fully enclosed crew compartment with rear entry doors and fitting a Bofors cupola with a 20 mm gun—mounted externally but fired from within by remote control.

Design of the Pbv 301 was initiated by S. Berge in 1954, in advance of a Swedish Army requirement for a tracked armoured carrier. However, two years later sanction was given for the construction of two prototypes, which were ready for trials in 1958, and in January 1960, a bulk order was given to A. B. Hägglund & Söner, of Ornsköldsvik, who carried out most of the conversions during 1962 and 1963.

While the Pbv 301 carriers were still being built work began on a new type, the Pbv 302 (Pl. 137). Outwardly, the Pbv 302 resembles the M113 and has similar amphibious capabilities. But it also has a turret with a 20 mm Hispano Suiza gun and openings in the roof of the crew compartment with hydraulically operated folding hatches, which enable all members of its crew to use their small arms. The Pbv 302 is, clearly, not intended to be a mere "battle taxi" but to meet requirements not far removed from the tactical concepts pioneered by the German Army and embodied in its HS-30 and Spz (neu) carriers.

Apart from its general characteristics the Pbv 302 has two design features which are peculiar to it. One is the location of its engine under the floor of the front portion of the vehicle, so that the driver, commander and turret gunner sit over it. The other and more significant feature is the adoption of a double skin hull whose relatively thin outer skin encloses additional volume required for buoyancy and which has provided an opportunity for shaping the hull to reduce its water resistance without compromising its ballistic characteristics (Pls. 138 and 138a).

Development and the subsequent production of the Pbv 302 have been the responsibility of A. B. Hägglund & Söner. Work on its design began in 1961 and testing of prototypes in January 1963; the first production vehicles were completed in 1966 in a newly built assembly plant which in the autumn of 1965 was still only an empty shell.

The U.S. Army has now also developed an amphibious armoured personnel carrier which represents a departure from its earlier "battle taxi" concept. The vehicle is the XM701 Mechanised Infantry Combat

Vehicle first built, in prototype form, in 1965 by the Pacific Car and Foundry Company, of Renton, Washington (Pl. 139). It is based on the well-tried chassis of the M107 and M110 self-propelled guns and, like the M59 and the M113, it is relatively bulky, as a result of being required to swim. But, in marked contrast to the two earlier carriers, it has firing ports in the sides of the superstructure and a two-man turret mounting a 20 mm gun and a 7·62 mm machine gun. As a combat vehicle the XM 701 appears inferior to the German Spz (neu) or the second Mowag Pirate but it shows that, after almost twenty years of being the leading exponent of the "battle taxi" concept, even the U.S. Army has recognised that infantry should be able to fight on the move from its carriers.

The Soviet Army appears to have done so earlier but has been slow in developing a real combat carrier. Its first tracked armoured personnel carrier, the BTR-50P, which came into service around 1955, is little more than a PT-76 amphibious reconnaissance tank with its turret replaced by a raised superstructure (Pl. 140). At first it did not even have overhead protection for its central compartment which is occupied by 12 out of its 15-man crew. The BTR-50P does, however, have an advantage in the amphibious characteristics which it has inhertied from the PT-76. As a result it can charge in and out of water at a speed impossible for the M113 or the Pbv 302 because of their low freeboard, or for the FV.432 because of its vulnerable flotation screen. Being provided with a water jet propulsion unit, the BTR-50P can also swim faster and manoeuvre in water more rapidly, which not only enables it to cross water obstacles more quickly but also to negotiate rivers flowing faster than those that track-propelled amphibians can tackle.

CHAPTER 10

Wheeled Armoured Vehicles

INTEREST in wheeled armoured vehicles has tended to fluctuate with the tempo and nature of military operations. They first sprang into prominence in the opening, mobile stages of the First World War, which favoured the employment of armoured cars for reconnaissance and raids. But when the fighting settled down to trench warfare the opportunities for the operation of armoured cars vanished, as there were no roads for them to run on and attempts to make them operate off the road led to another type of vehicle—the tank.

Towards the end of the First World War, when operations became more mobile, interest in armoured cars revived and it grew after the war, particularly from the point of view of police operations and cooperation with horse cavalry, for which the early tanks were not sufficiently mobile. As a result, armoured cars were widely used during the twenties and early thirties. They were, however, roadbound and their effectiveness was, consequently, limited. In the meantime the mobility of tanks improved considerably and with the appearance of the Vickers-Carden-Loyd light tanks they began to take over the functions performed earlier by armoured cars. Thus, the importance of armoured cars declined during the thirties and on the eve of the Second World War only the German and French Armies attached any importance to them.

The position changed again when the war broke out and the mobile operations of the German armoured forces revived interest in armoured cars, which were the basic vehicles of the reconnaissance units of the Panzer divisions. Further impetus to the development of armoured cars was provided by the experience of the British forces in Libya during 1940 to 1942. As a result, wheeled armoured vehicles began to be produced on a large scale both in Britain and the United States and at the time of the battle of El Alamein, in October 1942, the British forces in the Middle East had no less than 1,473 armoured cars compared with 2,671 tanks.

When the scene of the Anglo-American operations shifted in 1943 to

Italy the employment of armoured cars was sharply curtailed and even the return to more mobile warfare in North-West Europe in 1944, did not fully restore them to favour. In fact, immediately after the war the U.S. Army once again abandoned the development of wheeled armoured vehicles and for more than twenty years thereafter obstinately ignored their usefulness.

The attitude adopted by the U.S. Army at the end of the Second World War was not shared by the British and French Armies which rightly concluded that wheeled armoured vehicles had a continuing role to play. To do this, however, they had to be properly designed and not based on adaptations of car or truck chassis, as most of the armoured cars used during the Second World War still were. This included the M8 armoured car used by the U.S. Army, which was originally designed as the T22 37 mm anti-tank gun motor carriage mainly with a view to the ease of manufacture. Like other vehicles of this kind, the M8 was, therefore, economically attractive but its off-the-road performance and general characteristics inevitably fell short of what could be achieved by proper design.

What could be done by designing armoured cars from first principles was shown as early as 1929 by the Daimler-Benz ARW/MTW 1, or *Achtradwagen/Mannschaftstransportwagen* (Pl. 141). This experimental armoured car designed under the direction of Professor F. Porsche had eight wheels, all of which were driven and independently suspended, a self-supporting hull which eliminated the need for a chassis frame, and what is more, it was amphibious. A similar eight-wheeled vehicle was also built at the time by the C. D. Magirus company while Büssing-NAG developed a ten-wheeled vehicle. All three designs stemmed from a requirement issued in 1927 by the Army Ordnance Office of the Reichswehr Ministry and they were well ahead of all other contemporary designs. In fact, more than a quarter of a century had to pass before another wheeled armoured vehicle was produced which incorporated all the principal features of the ARW/MTW 1.

None of the three designs advanced beyond prototypes, for financial reasons, and for a time the German Army went back to the inferior type of armoured car based on truck chassis with only rear wheel drive and rigid beam axles. However, in 1935 work started at Büssing-NAG on a new eight-wheeled armoured car, with all-wheel drive and independent suspension, and this began to come into service in 1938 as a heavy reconnaissance vehicle. Its off-the-road performance was superior to that of other contemporary armoured cars and was, in fact, comparable to that of light tanks. In consequence it proved effective wherever the Panzer formations fought during the Second World War—in Western Europe, in Russia and in North Africa—and it continued to be produced right up to 1945. By then, however, the original Sd.Kfz.231 version was superseded by the improved Sd.Kfz.234, whose development was initiated in August 1940 with particular reference to operation in the tropics. Vehicles of the Sd.Kfz.234 series were consequently fitted with air-cooled V-12 Tatra diesels and one of them, the Sd.Kfz. 234/2 Puma, had a turret-mounted 50 mm high-velocity gun which, combined with its other characteristics, made it the most effective of all the armoured cars used up to the end of the Second World War (Pl. 142).

In the interval between the development of the Daimler-Benz ARW/MTW 1 and of the eight-wheeled Sd.Kfz.231 an eight-wheeled armoured car was also built in Austria by the Steyr-Daimler-Puch AG. The vehicle was the Austro-Daimler ADGZ, which was first built in 1934: it was more clumsy than the German eight-wheelers but it shared with them such essential points as multi-wheel drive and being designed from scratch as a wheeled armoured vehicle. Only 52 vehicles of this type were produced but its development was followed by that of two other all-wheel drive armoured cars, the six-wheeled ADKZ and the small turretless, 4 × 4 ADSK.

The union of Austria with Germany in 1938 put an end to the development of the Austro-Daimler armoured cars. But they left their mark as the result of the ADSK being tested in Britain, where, on the strength of its high standard of performance, it became a model for the Daimler Scout Car. Work on this small, turretless 4 × 4 vehicle started in 1937, at the B.S.A. Co Ltd., and it was produced from December 1939 onwards by the Daimler Co Ltd. Altogether 6,626 vehicles of this type were produced during the Second World War and they proved useful in a variety of scouting and liaison roles. The Scout Car also served as the basis for the design of a more effective, turreted vehicle, the Daimler Armoured Car. Mechanically, the Armoured Car was, in essense, a scaled-up version of the Scout Car. However, not only was it larger, weighing 6·8 instead of 2·8 tons, but it also carried effective armament in the form of a 40 mm 2-pounder gun, as well as a coaxial 7·92 mm Besa machine gun (Pl. 143).

The design of the Daimler Armoured Car started in April 1939, under the incongruous designation of "Tank, Light, Wheeled," but after it came into service in 1941 it proved successful as a reconnaissance vehicle. It was widely used as such during the latter part of the Second World War when it also distinguished itself as one of the most advanced and successful wheeled armoured vehicles from the automotive design point of view.

The automotive features of the two Daimler vehicles have been retained, with refinements, in the FV.701 Ferret, which has been produced by the Daimler Company in response to a 1947 War Office requirement for a successor to the original Scout Car. Thus, the Ferret has the same type of transmission layout with a fluid coupling, Wilson-type epicyclic gearbox, single central differential and parallel shafts on either side of the vehicle driving bevel gears at each of the four wheel stations and, thence, through Tracta-type constant velocity joints, the wheels. As before, the wheels are located by double transverse wishbones and are sprung by helical springs. The Ferret is, however, larger than its predecessors and, in particular, has a longer wheelbase, which makes it less prone to pitch over rough surfaces and thereby increases its average cross-country speed.

Like the original Scout Car, the Mark 1 Ferret is still turretless and, consequently, its usefulness has been limited. But the Mark 2 has been more sensibly provided with a turret (Pl. 144). The turret is only armed with a ·30 in Browning machine gun, but it has made the Ferret much more effective both for reconnaissance and security operations, the two principal fields of employment of the Ferrets since their entry into service with the British Army in 1951. In addition, 1,700 Ferrets were also delivered by the end of 1964 to several Commonwealth armies and others, including the French Army.

Since 1960 some Mark 2 Ferrets have been modified to carry Vickers Vigilant anti-tank guided missiles, one ready to fire mounted on each side of the turret and two more stowed alongside the hull (Pl. 145). More recently still, the Mark 2 has been developed into the Mark 4, which has larger tyres and a flotation screen as well as strengthened suspension components and disc, instead of drum, brakes. In consequence it is more mobile than the earlier model but, unaccountably, it is not better armed. However, the missile-carrying versions have been developed from the Mark 2/6 with its makeshift Vigilant installation into the Mark 5 which is a "big-wheeled" Ferret with a special turret carrying four Swingfire anti-tank guided missiles and two more stowed on the hull (Pl. 146).

In its Mark 4 version, which weighs 5·4 tons, the Ferret approaches the weight of the original Daimler Armoured Car and, given a bigger turret with better armament, it might well have been developed into its successor, as well as that of the Daimler Scout Car. Instead the Daimler Armoured Car has been replaced by the Alvis Saladin, whose development can also be traced back to 1947. Prototypes of the Saladin were not built, however, until 1952, and the first production vehicle until 1958.

The chassis design of the Saladin resembles that of the Daimler Scout and Armoured Cars but it has torsion bar springing and six, instead of four, wheels—the front four being steered. The use of three evenly spaced wheels per side represented a significant advance on the Daimler vehicles but it was not original, having been adopted earlier on armoured cars developed in the United States. In fact, by accident or design, the wheelbase, wheel-track and tyre size of the Saladin are the same as those of the U.S. M38 armoured car of 1945 (Pl. 147). This car, originally known as the T28, was developed by the Chevrolet Division of the General Motors Corporation from the earlier T19 6 × 6 armoured car and was accepted in March 1945, as a replacement for the M8. But it was never produced in quantity because shortly afterwards the U.S. Army decided to abandon armoured cars. Yet it was a very promising vehicle and in one respect at least it was superior to the Saladin, namely in weighing only 6·8 tons compared with the Saladin's 11·4 tons. The Saladin is, however, better armed, having a 76·2 mm instead of 37 mm gun, and it is also better armoured (Pls. 148–150).

Armament apart, the Saladin represents, in effect, a combination of the best features of the M38 and of the Daimler Armoured Car. As such it is superior to either of the two earlier vehicles but, by the same token, its design involved no major technological advance on the features proved in them. The eleven-year development period which preceded the delivery of the first production vehicle would have been totally incomprehensible, therefore, were it not for the fact that a derivative of the Saladin was given priority over it. This meant that the resources which might have been available for the development and production of the Saladin were devoted instead to the Saracen armoured personnel carrier, which was given priority because of the need around 1950 for this type of vehicle in the contemporary counter-guerilla operations of the British Army in Malaya (Pl. 151).

The chassis of the Saracen is virtually the same as that of the Saladin but with the in-line 8 cylinder Rolls-Royce B.80 engine moved to the front; its superstructure is entirely different, the body being designed to accommodate twelve men, including the driver. Prototypes of the

Saracen were built in 1950 and the first production vehicles were delivered in 1952. Subsequently, in addition to its use in Malaya and in security operations elsewhere, the Saracen became the standard infantry carrier in the British armoured brigades. Its characteristics corresponded to the contemporary British tactical doctrine of supporting tank regiments by rapidly rushing small bodies of infantry from one part of the battlefield to the other, instead of providing armoured brigades with a better proportion of infantry capable of close and sustained cooperation with tanks, for which a well-designed tracked armoured personnel carrier would have been more suitable. However, the Saracen has also been used in armoured car regiments, as a companion to the Saladin, for which it is much better suited.

Like the Ferret, the Saracen and the Saladin have been produced by Alvis Ltd., not only for the British Army but also for several others. Thus, some 450 Saracens and 300 Saladins were exported by mid-1964 and since then, in 1965–66, more Saladins were produced for the Federal German Border Police. During that period a new version of the Saladin was also developed. This carries a collapsible flotation screen which enables the vehicles fitted with it to cross water obstacles and greatly enhances their operational mobility.

In contrast, there has been little further interest in the Saracen, whose importance to the British armoured formations has decreased since the appearance of the FV.432 tracked carrier. At the same time some of its less exacting roles have been taken over by the FV.1611 1-ton Armoured Truck (Pl. 152). This vehicle was devised during the mid-fifties when the supply of Saracens was painfully inadequate and no tracked carrier had yet been developed. In other words, it was little more than a stop-gap and consisted of the chassis of an earlier 4 × 4 Humber truck fitted with an armoured body which was fully enclosed but which was ballistically poorly shaped. Nevertheless, 1,700 vehicles of this type were ordered in 1958 and it also served as the basis of the FV.1620 Hornet launcher for the Malkara anti-tank guided missiles, which came into service in 1962. Because of the cumbersome dimensions of the Malkara missiles, the Hornet can only carry four of them: two ready to fire on a launcher arm and two more, disassembled, under the arm. As Hornets are, clearly, limited-purpose vehicles only one squadron of the Royal Armoured Corps has been equipped with them, mainly for use in support of airborne operations where battle tanks cannot be brought in to oppose enemy armour but where Hornets could be delivered by parachute.

Quite different wheeled armoured vehicles have been developed in France. Their development stems from designs evolved before the Second World War to meet the requirements of the French Cavalry for reconnaissance vehicles. One of the most remarkable of these was an armoured car known originally as the Gendron-Poniatowski and later as the Gendron-Somua, after the designer and the S.O.M.U.A. company which built it (Pl. 153). This was a 6·5-ton vehicle whose appearance foreshadowed that of the Daimler Armoured Car. However, its outstanding feature was the running gear consisting of six wheels which were independently suspended and all of which could be driven. But the two centre wheels could also be disengaged and raised off the ground for more efficient road operation. On the other hand, when all six wheels were driven the Gendron-Somua could compete off the road with tracked vehicles. In fact, when it was first tried by the French Army in 1935, it outperformed the tracked Renault A.M.R. Model 1935 which was designed to the same requirement for an *auto-mitrailleuse de reconnaissance* and which resembled the then popular Vickers-Carden-Loyd light tanks.

The A.M.R. Gendron-Somua represented a major step forward in the development of armoured cars and it was to have been produced for the French Army. In fact, it never was as its manufacture was disrupted by the outbreak of the Second World War. In the meantime, a somewhat similar armoured car was developed by the S.A. des Anciens Etablissements Panhard & Levassor, a company whose record of producing wheeled fighting vehicles goes as far back as 1911. In 1932–33 it had already designed an advanced *auto-mitrailleuse de découverte*, the A.M.D. Panhard Model 178, a rear-engined, 4 × 4 armoured car, which was adopted by the French Army in 1935. Then, in 1937, it began to develop an even more advanced armoured car, the eight-wheeled Panhard Model 201. A prototype of this vehicle was built by 1940 but then France was defeated and the development of the Model 201 came to an end. The prototype was actually evacuated to what was then French North Africa but only to be lost in the Sahara and the drawings were destroyed.

The ideas embodied in the Model 201 were, however, revived after the liberation of France in 1944 and in July 1945 the French Army issued a requirement for an armoured car whose design followed that of the 201. This became the *Engin Blindé de Reconnaissance*, or E.B.R., Panhard Model 212 (Pl. 154). The first two prototypes of the new vehicle were completed in July 1948; production started two years later and continued until 1960, by which time the E.B.R. became the basic vehicle of the French armoured reconnaissance units and had been extensively employed in counter-guerilla operations in Algeria.

Apart from its eight large wheels, a feature of the E.B.R. is the almost complete symmetry of its layout. This stems from the adoption of two driver's stations, which mean that the E.B.R. can be driven backwards as easily as forwards—a desirable feature in wheeled armoured vehicles as they cannot be slewed round like tracked vehicles (Fig. XXIII). The symmetrical layout was made possible by the development of a special, horizontally opposed, 12-cylinder air-cooled engine only 8½ in high and mounting it under the floor in the centre of the hull. From the engine drive is taken through two gearboxes connected in series, giving a total of sixteen speeds, to a single central differential, which can be locked out, and then along each side of the hull to all eight wheels.

In contrast to the double, transverse wishbone of the Daimler and Alvis models, the front four wheels of the E.B.R. are mounted on leading arms and the rear four on trailing arms. All eight are independently sprung but the four outer ones have metallic, coil springs whereas the four inner wheels have simple hydro-pneumatic spring units. Moreover, whereas the four outer wheels are fitted with pneumatic tyres the four inner ones are solid tyred and heavily spudded, the difference being due to the fact that the inner wheels are not required for operation on roads and are normally raised clear off the road surface. The wheels are of larger diameter than those of other contemporary wheeled armoured vehicles and when all eight are in contact with the ground, and have penetrated it to a depth of 0·4 in, the pressure on the ground is only 10 lb/in^2, which not only makes the E.B.R. superior to other armoured cars but also to battle tanks.

In addition to its unusual automotive features, the E.B.R. also has a trunnion-mounted, or oscillating, turret. The original version had the F.L.11 turret mounting a 75 mm gun capable of firing armour-piercing projectiles with a muzzle velocity of 1,970 ft/sec. Subsequently a number of vehicles were fitted with the F.L.10 turret of the AMX 13 tank having a more powerful 75 mm gun with a muzzle velocity of 3,280 ft/sec (Pl. 155). However, the F.L.10 turret increased the weight of the E.B.R. from 13 to 15 tons and its overall height from 7 ft 4 in to 8 ft 6 in. In consequence, following the successful development of a 90 mm smooth bore gun, it was decided to refit all E.B.R. with the F.L.11 turret mounting the new gun (Pl. 156). The 90 mm gun fires

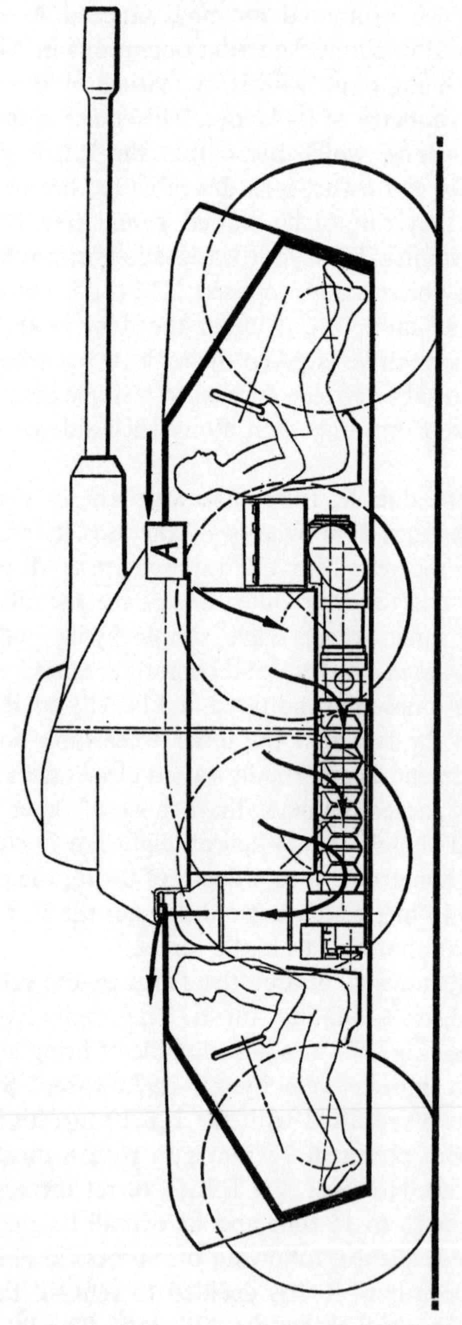

Fig. XXIII Cross section of the Panhard E.B.R.

fin-stabilised shaped-charge projectiles instead of the more conventional armour-piercing projectiles of the earlier 75 mm guns or the HESH projectiles on which the Saladin relies to defeat armour. The 90 mm projectiles are capable of penetrating armour 350 mm thick and they enable the E.B.R. to engage even battle tanks.

The excellent off-the-road performance, due to its length and eight large driven wheels, together with its armament makes the E.B.R. a very effective military vehicle. But, because of its size and sophistication, it has been expensive to produce and, in some respects, difficult to maintain. For instance, to remove the engine it is necessary to lift off first the whole turret assembly. Moreover, the E.B.R. is too heavy for many of the roles for which wheeled armoured vehicles are generally required. In particular, the experience gained by the French Army during the counter-guerilla operations in Algeria brought out the need for an armoured car less powerful than the E.B.R. but better armed than the Ferret scout cars which the French Army purchased from Britain. Out of this, in the spring of 1956, came a French Army requirement for what became known as the *Auto-mitrailleuse Légère*, or A.M.L., Panhard Model 245 (Pl. 157).

Prototypes of the A.M.L. were built by mid-1959 and by the end of 1961 one French regiment was already fully equipped with it. Since then many more A.M.L. have been produced, not only for the French Army but also for the armed forces of nine other nationalities. In addition, a substantial number of the A.M.L. has been built, under licence, in South Africa.

In some respects the A.M.L. is comparable to the Ferret. It is of approximately the same size and has four independently sprung wheels driven through a central differential. The central differential is, however, of a limited-slip cam-type and there is a similar differential in each of the side drive lines, acting between the front and rear wheels on its side. In contrast to the E.B.R., the front as well as the rear wheels are located on trailing arms, each wheel being sprung by means of a coil spring. Unlike the E.B.R., the A.M.L. has a rear-mounted engine, which is of an air-cooled 4-cylinder horizontally-opposed type and whose cylinders as well as other components are the same as those found in the two-cylinder engines of contemporary Panhard passenger cars.

The most significant difference between the A.M.L. and the Ferret is in the turrets and armament. Thus, in contrast to the one-man turret of the Ferret armed only with a machine gun, the A.M.L. has a larger, two-man turret of the H.E.60 or H.90 type. The H.E.60 mounts a 60 mm breech-loaded mortar and two 7·5 mm machine guns, an unusual combination of weapons derived from the French Army's experience in Algeria. The H.90 turret mounts a 90 mm D.E.F.A. 921A gun as well as a coaxial 7·5 mm machine gun (Pl. 158). The gun, which is essentially the same as that mounted more recently in the E.B.R., fires fin-stabilised shaped-charge projectiles with a muzzle velocity of 2,450 ft/sec and its installation has added a highly effective armament to the advantages of light weight and simplicity already possessed by the A.M.L.

Similar types of armament have been installed in an armoured car developed more recently in Belgium by the Fabrique Nationale d'Armes de Guerre S.A., the F.N. 4RM/62F A.B. (Pl. 160). One turret of this vehicle mounts a 60 mm mortar and two 7·62 mm machine guns, while another mounts a 90 mm smooth-bore CATI gun and one 7·62 mm machine gun. However, the F.N. armoured car is larger than the Panhard A.M.L., has rigid beam axles and has not been produced in any quantity.

No comparable, turreted vehicles have appeared so far in the Soviet Union. Instead, the Soviet Army has developed several wheeled armoured personnel carriers and has used them on an increasing scale since the end of the Second World War, their large scale production being facilitated by the inexpensive nature of most of them. In fact, the first two post-war vehicles, the four-wheeled BTR-40 and the six-wheeled BTR-152, have been no more than trucks with simple, open-top armoured bodies. Only in the sixties have they appeared fitted with overhead protection and, apart from the provision of driven front axles, the only advance on conventional truck chassis design embodied in them has been the provision on some of the late BTR-152 of a central tyre pressure control system (Pl. 161). This is by no means original but it enables the driver to change tyre pressures quickly, to suit the surface on which the vehicle is operating.

When it was introduced in the late forties, the BTR-152 became the first armoured personnel carrier to be furnished to the Soviety infantry and led to its large-scale mechanisation. It could carry up to 15 men and whatever its shortcomings it represented a considerable improvement on the unarmoured trucks used previously for carrying the infantry. The smaller BTR-40 has been used less extensively, mainly by reconnaissance units as a scout carrier, and in the late fifties it began to be replaced by a better vehicle, the BRDM (Pl. 162). Like the BTR-40, the BRDM still has rigid beam axles but it can float and it has a water jet propulsion unit, which enables it to cross relatively fast-flowing rivers. The same general characteristics are possessed by an improved, rear-engined version of the BRDM (Pl. 163). However, the latest version of this amphibious reconnaissance vehicle is not only fully enclosed, as the BRDM is, but is also fitted with a small machine gun turret.

A very much bigger step forward is represented by the BTR-60 armoured personnel carrier introduced around 1960 (Pl. 164). This has eight-wheel drive and independent suspension as well as the ability to float and a water jet propulsion unit. Its original version is still open-topped and its crew have to jump over the top to dismount but its cross-country performance is very much better than that of the BTR-152, which it is replacing, while its amphibious characteristics are sufficiently good for it to be used not only by army formations but also by the Soviet marines.

Since 1960 amphibious wheeled armoured vehicles have also been developed in the United States. Not by the U.S. Army, to be sure, but as private ventures of the Cadillac Gage Company and of the Defence Operations Division of the Chrysler Corporation. The Cadillac Gage Company has developed the Commando, a multi-purpose vehicle which has been fitted with a number of different turrets but which is also sufficiently roomy to act as a personnel carrier (Pl. 165). It can, in fact, carry as many as 12 men, including the driver. The turrets and the self-supporting hull have had to be specially developed but otherwise the design of the Commando has been based on commercially available components, in order to keep its cost to a minimum. For instance, its engine is a Chrysler model 361, as used in the M113 armoured personnel carrier, and its beam axles are of the type used in U.S. Army's M44 truck. As a result, the performance of the Commando leaves something to be desired off the road but its indifferent suspension is offset in part by its ability to float and paddle itself across calm inland waters at up to 4 m.p.h. (Pl. 166). This is remarkably high for a vehicle with nothing but its wheels to propel itself in water and can only be attained with new, well-treaded tyres. Its amphibious capabilities combined with low cost have made it an attractive proposition and in 1965 the U.S. Army ordered 200, under the XM706 designation, for use by the South Vietnamese forces.

The Chrysler Corporation has produced two vehicles. One is the MAC-1 four-wheeled armoured car produced in 1963 for Mexico (Pl. 167). It also uses standard truck chassis components, including beam-axles, for the sake of economy. Like the later versions of the

Commando it also has a one-man turret with a 20 mm Hispano Suiza gun, but in its standard form it is not amphibious. It has, however, a ballistically well-shaped hull. The second vehicle is the Special Warfare Armoured Transporter, or SWAT, which appeared in prototype form in 1966. This is a large multi-purpose vehicle with eight driven wheels, independent suspension and swimming capability, which is capable of carrying up to 12 men (Pl. 168).

An eight-wheeled armoured personnel carrier has also been developed in the Netherlands by the Van Doorne's Automobielfabriek N.V. (D.A.F.), of Eindhoven. The design of this vehicle, known as the YP-408, dates from 1956–1957, and is based on the chassis components of the earlier, D.A.F. YA-328 six-wheeled artillery tractor, from which it has inherited such advanced features as an "H" type drive line with a single central differential (Pl. 169). The "H" type transmission layout with shafts on each side of the vehicle and the self-supporting armoured hull have made it possible to lower the floor of the crew compartment on to the bottom plate of the hull, with the result that the YP-408 is only 5 ft 11 in high. An unusual feature of the YP-408 is that the second pair of wheels, which are additional to those of the YA-328, are steered but not powered. Their function, therefore, is merely to help to spread the load on the ground and to assist in the crossing of transverse ridge-type obstacles, traction being provided by the other six wheels.

Production of the YP-408, which commenced towards the end of 1963, was accompanied by the development of a second D.A.F. armoured vehicle, the YP-104. The chassis design of this vehicle, which has never advanced beyond the prototype stage, resembles that of the YA-104 in having a single central differential and the drive taken by universally-jointed shafts directly from bevel boxes at each side of the hull to worm and wormwheel boxes at the four wheels. In contrast to the Panhard, Daimler and Alvis vehicles with a single central differential, the drive to the front wheels of the YP-104, and also of the YP-408, can be disengaged. Each of the four wheels is located by two trailing arms, like the front wheels of the YP-408, but the springing is by means of coil springs instead of transverse torsion bars and the engine of the YP-104 is located at the rear. From the military point of view the YP-104 is comparable to the Ferret. It is larger, however, being able to accommodate a three-man crew; it has no turret but it can be driven backwards as well as forwards, there being a second steering wheel at the back of the crew compartment.

Double driving controls have also been provided on several wheeled armoured vehicles developed in Switzerland by the Mowag Motorwagenfabrik AG., of Kreuzlingen. Their development began in 1953, as a private venture, and has led to a series of four-wheeled models with similar, ballistically well-shaped armoured hulls.

The original model was intended to perform the functions of a tank destroyer and carried a Belgian-made 90 mm smooth-bore Mecar gun in an open mounting. More recent models include the MR 8-01 personnel carrier and the very similar MR 8-09 reconnaissance car with a turret mounting a high velocity 20 mm Oerlikon gun. All the vehicles of the series have common chassis components, which include rigid beam axles and leaf springs. Their only unusual automotive feature, apart from the second, rear driving station, is that all four wheels are steered as well as driven (Pl. 170).

Of the various models of the Mowag series, only the MR 8-01 has been produced in quantity. Twenty vehicles of this type were purchased by the German Government in 1959 and 1960, and subsequently more than 500 were produced under licence in Germany by the Büssing and Henschel companies for the Federal Border Police.

In the meantime Mowag developed the prototype of a four-wheeled amphibious carrier (Pl. 171). This still had rigid axles but these were of the Portal type, giving greater ground clearance. Instead of the Chrysler six-cylinder spark-ignition engine mounted at the rear of the earlier models it had a Mowag four-cylinder two-stroke compression ignition engine mounted amidships, under the floor of the crew compartment. It had no rear driving station but it had a rear loading ramp giving excellent access to the crew compartment, as on the U.S. M59 and M113 tracked carriers. Like the latter, it had sufficient buoyancy to float without any additional equipment but, in contrast to other recently developed amphibious armoured vehicles, it propelled itself in water by means of two screws. The screws were shrouded and mounted under the extreme rear bottom edge of the hull, and they have been claimed to give the Mowag carrier a water speed of 7½ to 9 m.p.h., which is higher than that of other contemporary amphibians (Pl. 172).

More recently still, in 1964, Mowag built yet another vehicle, the Roland, which bears a family resemblance to the MR 8 series (Pl. 173). It is smaller and lighter, however, and is intended for police rather than military operations. Its chassis design is conventional but it has special alternative bullet-proof tyres and its observation cupola is surmounted by a machine gun operated from within by remote control.

An armoured car which is only suitable for police work has been produced in 1965 by Short Brothers and Harland Ltd., of Newtownards, Northern Ireland. Like so many of the early armoured cars it consists, in essence, of a simple armoured body mounted on a truck chassis. The chassis is that of a Landrover $\frac{3}{4}$-ton 4 × 4 truck and the vehicle is, in consequence, called the Shorland. It does, however, possess all-round protection and a one-man turret with a ·30 in Browning machine gun (Pl. 174).

Useful as they might be under some circumstances, vehicles like the Shorland and the Mowag Roland cannot compare with the highly-developed armoured cars produced by Panhard and Alvis. Nor can they compete with tracked armoured vehicles in meeting the requirements of military operations, whereas the more sophisticated wheeled armoured vehicles can.

Most of the requirements for wheeled armoured vehicles originate from two types of military operations. They are ground reconnaissance and security, which includes surveillance of critical areas, counter-reconnaissance and counter-insurgency operations, fighting the less heavily armed hostile elements and internal security work. All these offer considerable scope for the use of wheeled armoured vehicles but some armies have, nevertheless, preferred to use tracked armoured vehicles. For instance, the U.S. Army has developed the M41 light tank for much the same role as that performed by the E.B.R. and Saladin armoured cars, while the Soviet Army has produced the PT-76 amphibious tank. The U.S. Army has also developed the M114 Command and Reconnaissance Vehicle, a small amphibious tracked carrier, as its counterpart of the Ferret while the German Army uses the Hotchkiss-built SPz.11-2 tracked carrier for similar purposes.

Where tracked vehicles have been adopted in preference to wheeled alternatives the principal reason has been their inherently superior performance in the more difficult types of terrain, such as wet clay soils. Off-the-road performance of the better-designed wheeled vehicles has, however, generally proved adequate. Moreover, such soils represent only a small part of a wide spectrum of operating conditions and the optimum solution is a matter of statistical adaptation to the environment. In other words, the optimum solution is less likely to be provided by a vehicle designed to meet the relatively infrequent extremes than by one which is best under most conditions. Once this is recognised, a well-designed wheeled armoured vehicle becomes a more attractive proposition than an equivalent light tracked vehicle.

Away from clay soils and peat bogs the advantages are almost all on the side of wheeled vehicles. They can move much faster on roads and their endurance on hard ground is greater because their rolling resistance, and hence their fuel consumption, is lower. They are also significantly quieter which means not only that they are less likely to reveal their approach but also that they are considerably less fatiguing to their crews. Their suspension characteristics also give a better ride and they generally require less maintenance. All these advantages are particularly important when vehicles are required to operate over long distances or for prolonged periods of time and, provided that they are combined with adequate off-the-road performance, they make wheeled armoured vehicles eminently suitable for reconnaissance and security work.

To possess an adequately high level of off-the-road performance wheeled vehicles must have independent suspensions and multi-wheel drive systems. The need for independent suspensions with large wheel movements has been clearly recognised in the design of the more sophisticated vehicles which possess, as a result, better traction over uneven ground, better ride and better steering control when travelling at speed over rough ground than vehicles with rigid beam axles and stiff springing. The advantages of multi-wheel drive have received less recognition. This shows in the predominance of four-wheeled vehicles, which do not possess as large a ground contact area as they could and should have. In consequence, they do not develop as high a net drawbar pull as they could. They are also liable to become immobilised by bellying on transverse ridge-type obstacles. To overcome the last problem Soviet four-wheeled amphibious vehicles have small wheels under the centre section of the hull but a far better solution all round is to add an intermediate pair of full-size driven wheels. In other words, a major improvement is achieved by adopting a six-wheeled configuration of the kind introduced with U.S. T19 armoured car of 1942, and subsequently developed in the M38 and the Alvis Saladin.

Increasing the number of wheels still further, to eight, eliminates the tendency to pitch which six-wheeled vehicles exhibit at times. But it also implies smaller diameter wheels, which is undesirable from the point of view of traction and obstacle crossing, and involves some further increase in complexity and weight.

Whatever the number of wheels, the most attractive layout of the drive from the power unit to the wheels is of the H-type, with a single central differential and shafts running fore and aft on each side of the vehicle. This has been used on the Panhard, Daimler, Alvis and D.A.F. vehicles and eliminates the possibility of wheel cross-spin, as well as making it possible to lower the height of the hull by placing the driver and the engine between, instead of above, the transmission shafts.

To improve traction still further, the Panhard A.M.L. has a limited slip central differential while on the E.B.R. there is provision for locking the central differential out altogether. A disadvantage of a single central differential is axle wind-up and greater tyre wear on hard surfaces. To overcome this limited slip cam-type differentials have been introduced on the A.M.L. between the front and rear wheels on each side side while the E.B.R. has a de Lavaud free-wheel differential between the front and the three rear wheels on each side, its main function being to prevent wind-up between the front and rearmost wheels when the vehicle is operating on roads and the two intermediate wheels are raised.

An alternative solution to the problem of transmission wind-up and tyre scrub with a single central differential has been adopted in the D.A.F. YP-408 and YP-104, where the drive to the front wheels can be disengaged by means of dog clutches. However, to be effective in vehicles with six evenly spaced wheels this approach requires the simultaneous raising and disengagement of the middle pair of wheels or, in other words, a vehicle convertible from 6 × 6 to 4 × 2 drive.

The H-type drive line layout also offers the possibility of introducing some form of skid steering which would enable wheeled vehicles to turn around in a confined space as tracked vehicles can and thus eliminate this relative disadvantage. Skid steering has actually been tried in Britain in a large, 20·7 ton experimental six-wheeled vehicle, the T.V. 1000 built by F.V.R.D.E. in 1959, but as an alternative to wheel steering instead of a supplement to it. Its advantage, apart from pivot turning, is a wider hull, because the wheels do not have to be turned, but this is outweighed by the disadvantages of lower maximum road speed with skid steering and inevitably greater tyre wear.

Wheeled armoured vehicles steered by articulation have also been considered and some were actually built in Italy during the mid-twenties on the basis of the Pavesi tractor. Interest in them revived in the United States as a result of the successful use of articulated wheeled vehicles for earth-moving but, although tests with vehicles of this type indicated that under extreme off-the-road conditions their performance would be superior to that of more conventional vehicles, they have failed to establish an overall advantage.

To return to the H-type transmission layouts with a single central differential, yet another advantage which they offer when used in vehicles with at least six evenly spaced wheels is that the vehicles can continue to move when one or even two of their tyres are shot or blown off, provided that the damaged wheels are not both at the front or rear, or on the same side. To this extent vehicles such as the Saladin are less vulnerable than tracked vehicles, which are completely immobilised when one of their tracks is broken. Pneumatic tyres are generally more vulnerable, however, than tracks, particularly to damage by small arms bullets. The usual attempts at reducing this vulnerability amount to the fitting of the so-called "run-flat" tyres which have side walls much stiffer than those of normal tyres and which can, as a result, be run for a limited distance after being punctured. An alternative solution has been adopted in a number of French armoured cars, including the E.B.R., which has Weil-Picard inner tubes with a large number of small cells permanently filled with gas at 40 to 60 lb/in^2.

Unfortunately, run-flat tyres and tyres with Weil-Picard tubes are relatively stiff and they lose thereby much of the virtue of pneumatic tyres. In consequence, a different approach has been adopted in the Panhard A.M.L. which is fitted with much more supple, Michelin XL, radial-ply tubeless tyres and Hutchinson inner tubes. Like the Weil-Picard, the Hutchinson tube contains a large number of small cells permanently inflated with gas but, unlike the Weil-Picard, it only partly fills the tyre. It does not, therefore, affect the functioning of the tyre under normal conditions and only comes into operation when the tyre is punctured, when it enables the damaged wheel to run for a limited distance.

Another recent attempt at a "bullet-proof" tyre is represented by the wheel fitted to the Mowag Roland which has a special narrow pneumatic tyre flanked by two light-alloy discs. In the event of a puncture the discs support the side walls of the tyre while vanes on the outside of them assist traction in muddy terrain and they could also increase the propulsive effect of the wheels in water.

In the great majority of independent suspensions wheels have been located by means of double transverse links, or wishbones. These are very attractive structurally but they produce complications in the drive to the wheels, because of the angular movements of the drive shafts and changes in their length. The principal alternative to the double transverse links are trailing or leading arms which not only locate the wheels but, as in the case of the Panhard E.B.R. and A.M.L., contain a train of gears transmitting the drive to the wheels. In this form trailing, or leading, arm suspensions offer at least three important advantages over the transverse link systems. First, they eliminate the need for wheel drive shafts with sliding splined joints, which can be troublesome. Second, they reduce the number of constant velocity joints required per vehicle: for instance, the A.M.L. needs only two compared with the Ferret's eight. Third, they make it possible to bring the hull out much closer to the non-steered wheels and thereby reduce the disadvantage at which wheeled vehicles stand in relation to tracked ones on account of their narrower hulls (Figs. XXIV and XXV).

In addition to a well-developed independent suspension and multi-wheel drive wheeled armoured vehicles must also be as light as possible if they are to compete successfully with tracked vehicles off the road. In the past light weight implied indifferent armament but this no longer need apply, although some vehicles, such as the Ferret with its ·30 in machine gun, are still poorly armed. Several others are armed with 20 mm guns which enables them to fight other light armoured vehicles. High velocity guns of 30 mm would be better still but even they would not provide an effective defence against tanks.

One solution to the problem of an adequate anti-tank armament is provided by guided missiles. An early example of their application is provided by the Ferret with a Vigilant missile on either side of its turret. Another and better installation is illustrated by the A.M.L. with four *Entac* missiles on a S.A.M.O. 1160 launcher: the missiles are normally stowed behind the turret but for firing the launcher brings them out, in pairs, on either side of the turret. Yet another installation is indicated by the mock-up turret with four Swingfire missiles mounted on the Mark 5 Ferret.

The alternative to supplementing small-calibre high-velocity guns with guided missiles is to replace them by larger-calibre medium-velocity guns capable of firing both shaped charge and high explosive projectiles and yet compatible with a relatively low vehicle weight. The best example of this is provided by the A.M.L. which mounts a 90 mm smooth-bore gun and weighs only 5·6 tons.

Heavier vehicles can, of course, mount even more powerful armament. For instance, a wheeled armoured vehicle of about 15 tons could mount a large-calibre gun/missile launcher of the kind installed in the M551 Sheridan tank and thus carry the same armament as battle tanks. Vehicles as powerful and heavy as this are not, however, necessary for the reconnaissance and security roles for which wheeled armoured vehicles are best suited while other roles, involving heavy fighting, are best left to tanks. Any attempt to fulfill too many roles with a single

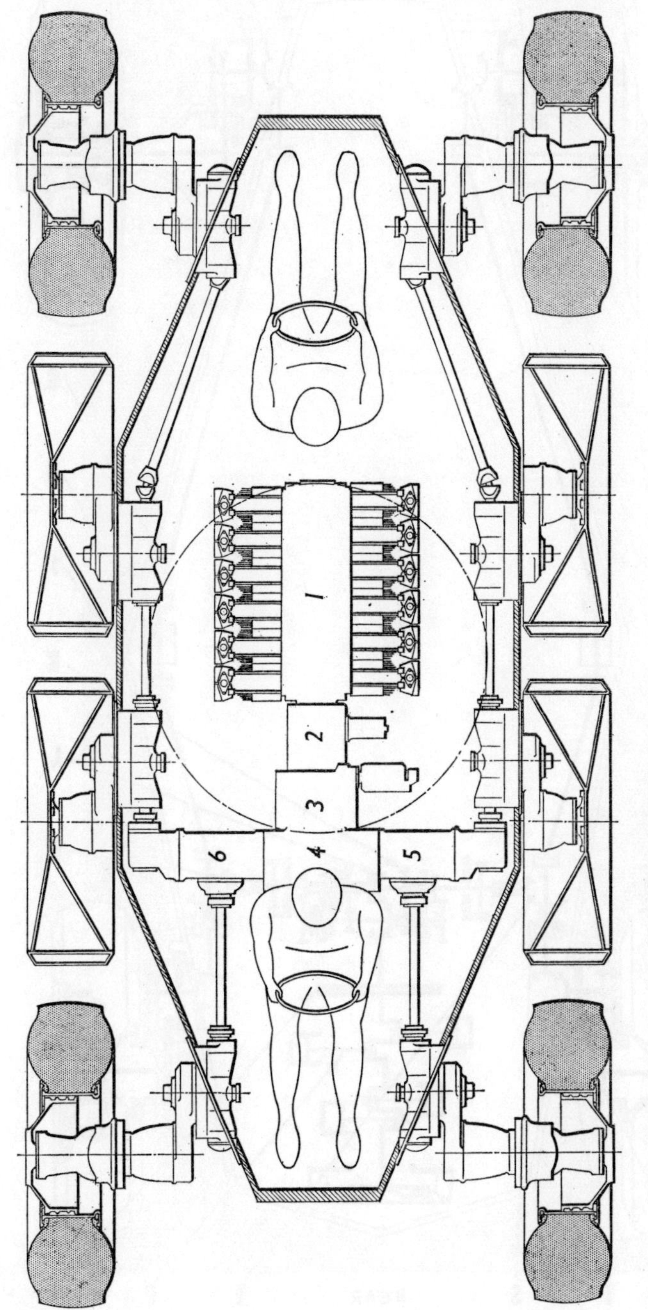

Fig. XXIV Plan view of the Panhard E.B.R. transmission:

1. Engine
2. Clutch
3. First gearbox
4. Second gearbox with differential

5 and 6. Free-wheel differentials.

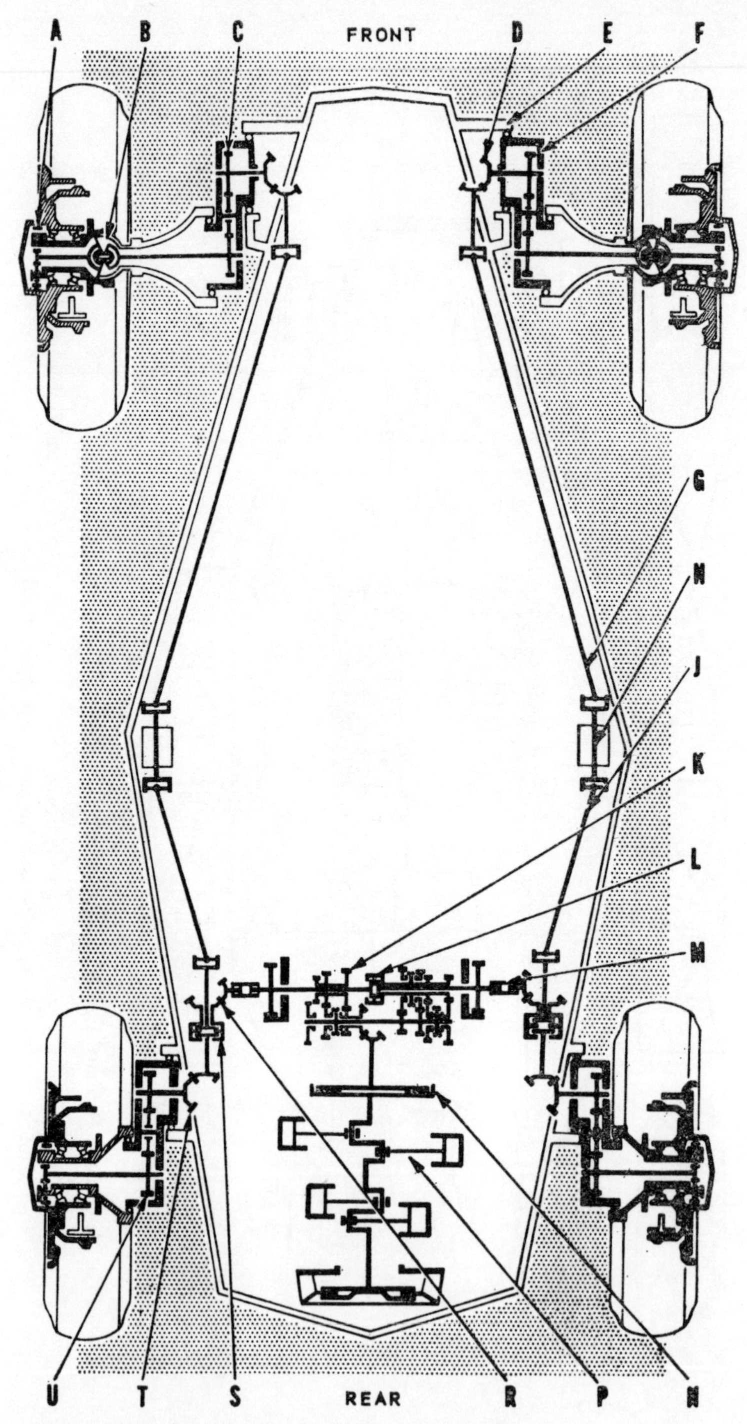

Fig. xxv Plan view of the Panhard A.M.L. transmission:

A – epicylic hub reduction gears
B – constant velocity joint
C and U – suspension arm gears
D and T – bevel gears
E – suspension arm bearing
F – suspension arm
G and J – drive shafts
H – intermediate shaft
K – gearbox
L – central differential
M – toothed coupling
N – centrifugal clutch
P – engine
R – bevel gears
S – side differential

vehicle can only lead to the kind of unsatisfactory compromise exemplified by most light tanks built to date: neither a good fighting vehicle nor a good reconnaissance vehicle.

If wheeled armoured vehicles are to be as light as possible they cannot, obviously, carry heavy armour. They must, however, have enough to be immune to rifle-calibre bullets and thus be able to move about more freely than unarmoured vehicles can in face of snipers or machine-gun fire. Anything much heavier and certainly anything above the level of immunity provided by the Ferret and the A.M.L. is highly questionable, for any practicable increase in armour protection will only extend the immunity to relatively few more weapons. At the same time it will impose a disproportionate penalty in terms of increased weight, which is most undesirable from several points of view, including that of the amphibious capability essential for reconnaissance vehicles.

Given sound designs, there is little doubt that wheeled armoured vehicles can meet the requirements of ground reconnaissance and security operations. Both types of operations are of major importance whenever ground forces are deployed and the need to perform them is unlikely to diminish in the foreseeable future. Indeed, the importance of security operations is bound to increase while political tensions continue and large scale military operations are inhibited by fears of the nuclear holocaust. In consequence, wheeled armoured vehicles are needed both by the major armies and by the defence forces of the smaller countries.

APPENDIX

Tables of Vehicle Data

Table

Country	*Britain*	*Britain*	*Britain*	*France*	*Germany*
Model	*Centurion Mark 10*	*Chieftain*	*Vickers 37-ton*	*AMX 30 (prototype)*	*Leopard*
Main armament, calibre, mm	105	120	105	105	105
Primary anti-tank round, type	APDS	APDS	APDS	HEAT	APDS & HEAT
Number of rounds	63	53	44	56	60
Fire control system, type	RMG	RMG	RMG	ORF	ORF
Weight, laden, tons	51	51·5	37·5	33	39·3
Overall dimensions					
length, vehicle only	25′ 8″	25′ 1″	23′ 11″	20′ 11″	22′ 0″
width	11′ 1″	11′ 6″	10′ 5″	10′ 2″	10′ 8″
height	9′ 9″	9′ 6″	—	8′ 3″	—
Height to turret roof	8′ 7″	8′ 0″	8′ 0″	7′ 6″	7′ 10″
Ground clearance	1′ 8″	—	1′ 4″	1′ 6″	1′ 6″
Engine, make	Rolls-Royce	Leyland	Leyland	SOFAM	Daimler-Benz
model	Meteor Mk. 4	L.60	L.60	12GSds	MB 838 Ca
gross b.h.p.	635	700	700	720	830
Max. road speed, m.p.h.	21·5	25	30/35	40	40
Range on roads, miles	115	250	220	300	380
Nominal ground pressure, lb/in²	13	14	12·8	10·8	12·3
Crew	4	4	4	4	4

RMG = Ranging Machine Gun
ORF = Optical Range Finder
CG = Command Guidance (Missiles)

I

Japan	*Soviet Union*	*Sweden*	*Switzer-land*	*U.S.A.*	*U.S.A.*	*U.S.A.*	*France*
Type 61	*T-54*	*Strv 103*	*Pz.61*	*M48A2*	*M60*	*M551*	*AMX 13 Model 58*
90 APC	100 APC	105 APDS	105 APDS	90 APC & APCR	105 APDS & HEAT	152 HEAT	105 HEAT
—	35	50	—	60	63	20 + 10 missiles	32
ORF	—	—	ORF	ORF	ORF	CG	—
34·4	36	36·5	36·5	47	47	15	15
20′ 8″	19′ 8″	22′ 8″	21′ 11″	21′ 6″	21′ 9″	20′ 8″	16′ 0″
9′ 8″	10′ 9″	10′ 10″	10′ 0″	11′ 11″	11′ 11″	9′ 2″	8′ 2″
—	7′ 11″	7′ 0″	8′ 11″	10′ 2″	10′ 6″	8′ 0″	7′ 6″
8′ 2″	—	6′ 3″	8′ 1″	—	—	7′ 7″	—
1′ 4″	1′ 5″	1′ 8″	1′ 5″	1′ 3″	1′ 6″	1′ 7″	1′ 2″
Mitsubishi	—	Rolls-Royce & Boeing	Daimler-Benz	Continental	Continental	GM	SOFAM
12 HM	V-2	K.60 & 553	MB 837	AVI-1790-8	AVDS-1790	6V-53T	8Gxb
600	580	240 + 490	630	865	750	300	245
28	34	25/30	30	30	30	43	37
—	220	200/250	190	160	300	370	220/250
13·5	11·8	12·8	12·2	11·9	11·3	6·8	10·8
4	4	3	4	4	4	4	3

Table

Country	*U.S.A.*	*U.S.A.*	*U.S.A.*	*Britain*	*Sweden*
Model	*M75*	*M59*	*M113*	*FV.432*	*Pbv.302*
Weight, laden, tons	18·75	19	10·5	15	13·3
Overall dimensions					
length	17′ 0″	18′ 5″	15′ 11″	16′ 9″	17′ 10″
width	9′ 4″	10′ 8″	8′ 10″	9′ 9″	9′ 4″
height	9′ 0″	9′ 1″	7′ 2″	7′ 2″	8′ 3″
Height to hull roof	—	8′ 7″	6′ 0″	6′ 2″	—
Ground clearance	1′ 6″	1′ 6″	1′ 4″	1′ 4″	—
Engine, make	Conti-nental	GM	Chrysler	Rolls-Royce	Volvo
model	AO-985-4	302	75M	K.60	—
gross b.h.p.	375	2 × 145	209	240	270
Max. road speed, m.p.h.	44	32	40	32	40
Range on roads, miles	115	120	200	360	220
Nominal ground pressure, lb/in²	8·2	7·75	7·5	11·3	7·8
Amphibious	No	Yes	Yes	After pre-paration	Yes
Turret gun	None	None	None	None	20 mm
Crew	12	12	13	12	12

II

France	*Germany*	*Germany*	*Austria*	*Switzer-land*	*Japan*	*U.S.A.*	*U.S.A.*
AMX-VTT	*HS.30*	*HW-K11*	*4K4F*	*Pirate*	*SU*	*XM701*	*LVTP5*
14	14·6	11	12·5	18·5	12	24·2	39·2
18′ 8″	18′ 3″	16′ 7″	17′ 7″	20′ 0″	15′ 11″	20′ 5″	29′ 8″
8′ 10″	8′ 4″	8′ 4″	8′ 3″	9′ 6″	7′ 11″	10′ 4″	11′ 8″
7′ 10″	6′ 1″	—	—	6′ 10″	5′ 7″	9′ 5″	8′ 7″
6′ 11″	5′ 4″	5′ 2″	5′ 5″	5′ 11″	—	6′ 10″	—
1′ 7″	1′ 5″	1′ 5″	1′ 4″	1′ 4″	1′ 4″	1′ 6″	1′ 6″
SOFAM	Rolls-Royce	Chrysler	Saurer	Mowag	Mitsubishi	GM	Conti-nental
8Gxb	B·81	75M	4F	M10DV	8HA21WT	8V-71T	LV-1790-1
270	235	210	220	430	240	425	810
38	40	40	37	40	28	38	30
220	250	200	230	250	125	400	250
10	9·8	7·8	7·3	9·4	—	11·3	9·2
No	No	No	No	No	No	Yes	Yes
7·5 mm	20 mm	None	None	20 mm	None	20 mm & 7·62 mm	·30 in
13	8	12	10	12	10	12	37

Table

Make	*Daimler*	*Daimler*	*Panhard*	*Daimler*	*Chevrolet*
Model	*Ferret Mark 2*	*Ferret Mark 4*	*A.M.L. Model 61*	*Daimler Mark II*	*M38*
Weight, laden, tons	4·3	5·35	4·7	7·5	6·83
Drive, type	4 × 4	4 × 4	4 × 4	4 × 4	6 × 6
Tyre size	9.00 × 16	11·00 × 20	11·00 × 16	10·50 × 20	12·00 × 20
Wheelbase	7′ 6″	7′ 6″	8′ 2″	8′ 6″	9′ 10″
Track	5′ 1″	5′ 9″	5′ 4″	6′ 6″	6′ 8″
Overall dimensions					
length, vehicle only	12′ 7″	13′ 0″	12′ 5″	13′ 0″	16′ 9″
width	6′ 3″	7′ 0″	6′ 5″	8′ 0″	8′ 0″
height	6′ 2″	6′ 8″	6′ 6″	7′ 4″	6′ 6″
Ground clearance	1′ 1″	—	1′ 1″	1′ 4″	1′ 2″
Engine, make	Rolls-Royce	Rolls-Royce	Panhard	Daimler	Cadillac
model	B.60	B.60	4HD	—	42
gross b.h.p.	116	129	89	95	148
Max. road speed, m.p.h.	58	—	56	50	60
Range on roads, miles	190	190	370/400	150/250	300
Turret armament					
gun	None	None	60 mm mortar	40 mm	37 mm
machine gun	·3 in	·3 in	2 × 7·5 mm	7·92 mm	·3 in
Crew	2	2	3	3	4

III

Alvis	*Büssing*	*Panhard*	*Alvis*	*D.A.F.*	*Chrysler*	*Mowag*	*Cadillac Gage*
Saladin	*Sd.Kfz. 234/2 Puma*	*E.B.R. Model 51*	*Saracen*	*YP.408*	*MAC-1*	*MR 8-09*	*Commando*
11·4	10·8	13	10	9·8	6·7	8·2	6·35
6 × 6	8 × 8	8 × 8	6 × 6	8 × 6	4 × 4	4 × 4	4 × 4
12.00 × 20	270-20	14·00 × 24	11·00 × 20	11·00 × 20	11·00 × 20	10·00 × 20	14·00 × 20
10′ 0″	13′ 1″	14′ 3″	10′ 0″	16′ 5″	9′ 4″	8′ 6″	8′ 9″
6′ 10″	6′ 5″	6′ 9″	6′ 8″	6′ 10″	—	6′ 5″	6′ 1″
16′ 2″	19′ 9″	18′ 2″	15′ 11″	20′ 0″	17′ 3″	17′ 5″	18′ 8″
8′ 5″	7′ 9″	7′ 11″	8′ 3″	7′ 10″	8′ 0″	7′ 3″	7′ 5″
7′ 10″	7′ 6″	7′ 4″	8′ 1″	6′ 0″	6′ 11″	8′ 0″	7′ 2″
1′ 5″	1′ 2″	1′ 4″	1′ 5″	1′ 6″	—	1′ 0″	1′ 4″
Rolls-Royce	Tatra	Panhard	Rolls-Royce	D.A.F.	Chrysler	Chrysler	Chrysler
B.80	103	12H6000	B.80	DS.575	HT 361	R 318	361
170	210	200	170	165	190	161	190
45	53	62	43	51	65	50	65
250	380	400	240	310	300	—	550
76 mm	50 mm	75 mm	None	None	20 mm	20 mm	None
·3 in	7·92 mm	7·5 mm	·3 in	None	None	None	·5 in & ·3 in
3	4	4	12	12	4	3–4	12

Bibliography

ANONYMOUS, *Illustrated Record of German Army Equipment*. Vol. III (Armoured Fighting Vehicles), War Office, London, 1947.

Sowiecka Broń Pancerna. Warszawska Dywizja Pancerna, Italy, 1945.

Tank Data. U.S. Army Ordnance School, Aberdeen Proving Ground, 1958.

Tank Museum Guide. Parts 1 to 5. Royal Armoured Corps Centre, Bovington Camp, *c*.1948–57.

ANDRONIKOW, I. G., and MOSTOWENKO, W. D. *Die Roten Panzer*, Lehmanns Verlag, München, 1963.

ANTONOV, A., ARTAMONOV, B., KOROBKOV, B., and MAGNIDOVICH, E. *Tank*. Ministerstva Oboroni Soyuza SSR, Moscow, 1954.

BARNES, G. M. *Weapons of World War II*. Van Nostrand, New York, 1947.

BEKKER, M. G. *Theory of Land Locomotion*. University of Michigan Press, Ann Arbor, 1956.

Off-the-Road Locomotion. University of Michigan Press, Ann Arbor, 1960.

DEYGAS, F. J. *Les Chars d'Assaut*. Charles-Lavauzelle, Paris, 1937.

DUTIL, L. *Les Chars d'Assaut*. Berger-Levrault, Paris, 1919.

DUVIGNAC, A. *Histoire de l'Armée Motorisée*, Imprimerie Nationale, Paris, 1948.

FERRÉ, G. *Le Défaut de l'Armure*. Charles-Lavauzelle, Paris, 1948.

FULLER, J. F. C. *Tanks in the Great War 1914-1918*. John Murray, London, 1920.

GILLIE, M. H. *Forging the Thunderbolt*. Military Service Publishing Co., Harrisburg, 1947.

GUDERIAN, H. *Panzer Leader*. Michael Joseph, London, 1952.

HACKER, O. H., ICKS, R. J., MERKER, O., and ZEZSCHWITZ, G. P. von. *Heigls Taschenbuch der Tanks*. Parts I and II. Lehmanns Verlag, München, 1935.

HARA, T., and TAKEUCHI, A. *Japanese Tanks and Fighting Vehicles*. Shuppan Kyodo, Tokyo, 1961.

HARA, T., and EIMORI, D. *Japanese Tanks and Armoured Vehicles*. Shuppan Kyodo, Tokyo, 1961.

HEIGL, F. *Taschenbuch der Tanks*. Lehmanns Verlag, München, 1926.

Taschenbuch der Tanks. Lehmanns Verlag, München, 1927.

ICKS, R. J. *Tanks and Armored Vehicles*. Duell, Sloan and Pearce, New York, 1945.

INOMA, S. *Sensha*. Sankai-do, Tokyo, 1941.

JONES, R. E., RAREY, G. H., and ICKS, R. J. *The Fighting Tanks since 1916*. National Service Publishing Co., Washington, 1933.

KUTZ, C. R. *War on Wheels*. Scientific Book Club, London, 1942

LIDDELL HART, B. H. *The Tanks: The History of the Royal Tank Regiment*, Cassell, London, 1959.

MAGNUSKI, J. *Wozy Bojowe 1914–1964*. Wydawnictwo Ministerstwa Obrony Narodowej, Warsaw, 1964.

MARTEL, G. le Q. *In the Wake of the Tank*. Sifton Praed, London, 1931.

OGORKIEWICZ, R. M. *Armour*. Stevens, London, 1960, and Frederick Praeger, New York 1960.

I Corazzati. Istituto per la Divulgazione della Storia Militare, Rome, 1964.

POSTAN, M. M. *British War Production*. H.M.S.O. and Longmans, London, 1952.

POSTAN, M. M., HAY, D., and SCOTT, J. D. *Design and Development of Weapons*. H.M.S.O. and Longmans, London, 1964.

PUGH, S. *Fighting Vehicles and Weapons of the Modern British Army*. Macdonald, London, 1962.

PUGNANI, A. *Storia della Motorizzatione Militare Italiana*. Roggero & Tortia, Torino, 1951.

RINEHART, J. S., and PEARSON, J. *Behavior of Metals under Impulsive Loads*. American Society of Metals, Cleveland, 1954.

SENGER und ETTERLIN, F. M. von. *Taschenbuch der Panzer 1943–1957*. Lehmanns Verlag, München. 1957.

Die Panzergrenadiere. Lehmans Verlag, München, 1961.

The World's Armoured Fighting Vehicles. Macdonald, London, 1962.

Das kleine Panzerbuch. Lehmanns Verlag, München, 1964.

Die deutschen Panzer 1926–1945. Lehmanns Verlag, München, 1965.

Die Kampfpanzer von 1916–1966. Lehmanns Verlag, München, 1966.

STERN, A. G. *Tanks 1914–1918*. Hodder and Stoughton, London, 1919.

SUETER, M. *The Evolution of the Tank*. Hutchinson, London, 1937.

SWINTON, E. D. *Eyewitness*. Hodder and Stoughton, London, 1932.

WARNICK, W. L., COOK, J. G., and BAKER, R. A. *The Tank Commander's Guide*, Stackpole, Harrisburg, 1963.

WHITE, B. T. *British Tanks 1915–1945*. Ian Allan, London, 1963.

British Armoured Cars 1914–1945. Ian Allan, London, 1964.

German Tanks and Armoured Vehicles 1914–1945. Ian Allan, London, 1966.

WORLEY, M. L. *New Developments in Army Weapons, Tactics, Organization and Equipment*. Military Service Publishing Co., Harrisburg, 1958.

ZEZSCHWITZ, G. P. von. *Heigls Taschenbuch der Tanks*. Part III, Lehmanns Verlag, München, 1938.

Index

1 – The first armed motor vehicle, a powered quadricycle with a Maxim machine-gun, being demonstrated by F. R. Simms in June 1899.

2 – Fowler armoured road locomotive and armour-plated wagons built in 1900.

3 – Simms' War Car at the Crystal Palace in London in April 1902.
4 – Rolls-Royce armoured car built in 1914 for the Royal Naval Air Service.

5 – The first tracked armoured vehicle consisting of a Delaunay-Belleville armoured car body on a Killen-Strait tractor.

6 – Little Willie, the first British tank, completed in September 1915.

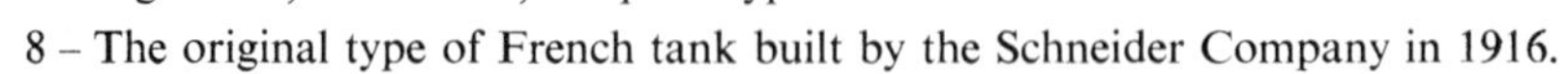

7 – Big Willie, or Mother, the prototype of the first tanks used in battle.

8 – The original type of French tank built by the Schneider Company in 1916.

9 – Renault F.T. light tank of 1918.

10 – M1917 light tank, a United States copy of the Renault F.T., and, right, an Anglo-American Mark VIII heavy tank.

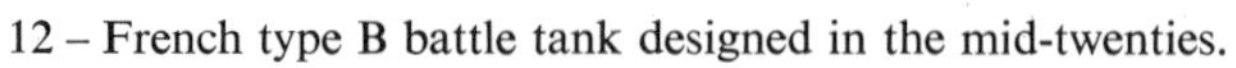

11 – French 2C heavy tank with a turret-mounted 75 mm gun.
12 – French type B battle tank designed in the mid-twenties.

13 – British Light Infantry Tank which attained 30 m.p.h. during trials in 1922.

14 – Vickers Medium Mark I.

15 – British Independent heavy tank with five turrets.

16 – British Medium Mark III tank with three turrets.

17 – Carden Loyd Mark VI tankette with head covers.

18 – Polish TKS tankettes developed from the Carden Loyd Mark VI.

19 – Light Tank Mark I built by Vickers-Armstrongs in 1930.
20 – Russian T-38 amphibious light tanks.

21 – Vickers-Armstrongs 6-ton tank, single turret model.

22 – Russian T-26C developed from the Vickers-Armstrongs 6-ton tank.

23 – Landsverk 10, or Strv m/31, light-medium tank of 1930.

24 – Ceskomoravska Kolben Danek tank assembled in Switzerland as the Pz. 39.

25 – United States T3 medium tank built by J. W. Christie in 1931.
26 – Russian Christie-type BT-7 tank.

27 – French H-35 light infantry tank.
28 – British Infantry Tank Mark I.

29 – Pz.Kpfw. II with a 20 mm gun, the most numerous German tank during the 1940 campaign in France.

30 – German Pz.Kpfw. IV 75 mm gun tank of 1939–1941.

31 – Russian T-34 medium tank.
32 – Russian KV-1 heavy tank.

33 – German Panther medium tank with a 75 mm L/70 gun.

34 – German Tiger II heavy tank with an 88 mm L/71 gun (side plates partly removed to reveal internal layout).

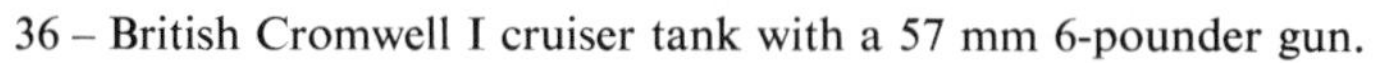

35 – British Churchill II infantry tank with a 40 mm 2-pounder gun.
36 – British Cromwell I cruiser tank with a 57 mm 6-pounder gun.

37 – Pilot model of the U.S. M3 medium tank with a hull-mounted 75 mm gun.

38 – United States M4A1 medium tank with a 75 mm gun.

39 – United States M4A3 medium tank with a 76 mm gun.

40 – United States M26 heavy tank with a 90 mm gun.

41 – British Centurion 1 with a 76·2 mm 17-pounder gun.

42 – Centurion 7 with an 83·4 mm 20-pounder gun.

43 – Centurion 9 with a 105 mm gun.
44 – Conqueror 120 mm heavy gun tank.

45 – Russian T-34/85 medium tank.

46 – Russian T-54 medium tank with a 100 mm gun.

47 – Russian-designed T-54 tank delivered by China to Pakistan in 1966.
48 – Russian T-62 battle tanks with 115 mm guns.

49 – Prototype of the AMX 50 battle tank with a 100 mm gun.
50 – French AMX 50 battle tank with a 120 mm gun.

51 – United States M46 medium tank.

52 – United States M103 120 mm gun heavy tank.

53 – Four tanks built in the United States during the fifties: left to right, M103 120 mm gun tank, M48 and M47 90 mm gun tanks and M41 76 mm gun light tank.

54 – United States M48A2 90 mm gun tanks.

55 – United States T95 medium tank.

56 – United States M60 105 mm gun battle tank.

57 – Japanese Type 61 medium tank.

58 – Swiss Pz.58 tank with a 90 mm gun.

59 – Swiss Pz. 61 tank with a 105 mm gun.

60 – Prototype of the French AMX 30 battle tank.

61 – Production version of the AMX 30 battle tank.

62 - Prototype of the German Leopard battle tank.

63 – Production version of the Leopard battle tank.

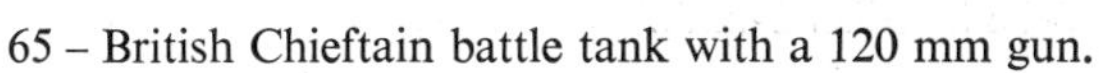

64 – Vickers 37-ton battle tank built for the Indian Army.

65 – British Chieftain battle tank with a 120 mm gun.

66 – Pre-production version of the Swedish S-tank.

67 – S-tank, or Strv 103.

68 – Swiss G-14 version of the German-designed and Czech-produced Jagdpanzer 38t of the mid-forties.

69 – Jagdpanzer (Kanone) built for the German Army during the early sixties.

70 – United States M60A1E1 battle tank with a 152 mm gun/missile launcher.

71 – United States M551 Sheridan air-transportable reconnaissance vehicle with a 152 mm gun/launcher.

72 – British Tetrarch, the first tank to go into action by air, being loaded into a Hamilcar glider.

73 – United States T9E1 prototype of the M22, the first tank designed and built for airborne operations.

74 – French AMX 13 light tank.

75 – AMX 13 light tank being unloaded from a Breguet Deux Ponts aircraft.

76 – T41 prototype of the U.S. M41 light tanks.

77 – United States T92 light tank.

78 – Russian PT-76 amphibious reconnaissance tank.

79 – United States M551 Sheridan being dropped by parachute from a transport aircraft.

80 – Chieftain tank armed with a high-velocity 120 mm gun.

81 – M50 Ontos armed with six 106 mm recoilless guns.

82 – SS-11 guided missile fired from a Hotchkiss light carrier.

83 – AMX 13 tank with SS-11 missiles.

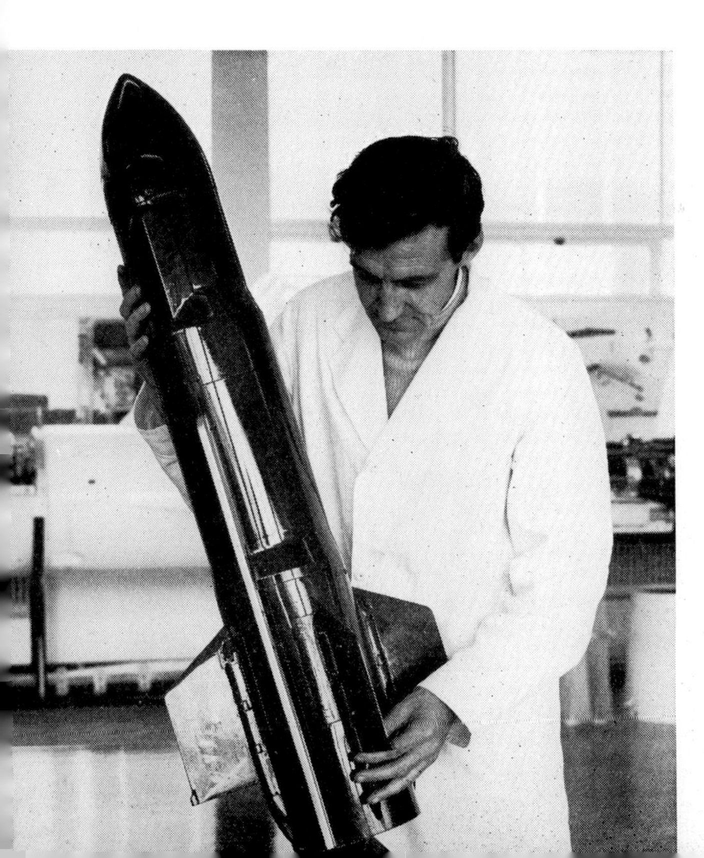

84 – Malkara missile fired from a FV.1620 Hornet.

85 – Swingfire, a second generation anti-tank guided missile.

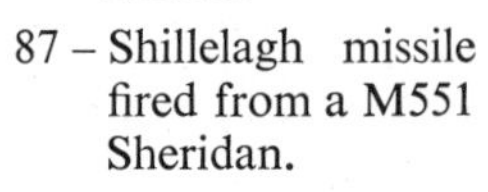

86 – Shillelagh guided missile.

87 – Shillelagh missile fired from a M551 Sheridan.

88 – Prototype of the AMX 13 tank with a F.L.10 trunion-mounted, or oscillating, turret.

89 – AMX 13 with a F.L.12 oscillating turret mounting a 105 mm gun.

90 – United States T92 tank with a cleft turret.

91 – United States M60A1E1 tank with a 152 mm gun/launcher mounted in a turret with reduced frontal area.

92 – Prototype of the U.S. M60A1 battle tank with an elongated turret surmounted by a machine-gun cupola.

93 – S-tank compared with a conventional, turreted, Centurion tank.

94 – United States M41 tank with welded turret and hull.

95 – United States T48 tank with a one-piece cast turret and hull.

96 – United States T196 (later M109) 155 mm self-propelled howitzer with a turret and hull welded out of aluminium alloy armour.

97 – United States T235 175 mm self-propelled gun with nylon blanket protection.

98 – Russian T-34 tank with a Christie type suspension.

99 – Horstmann-type bogie suspension and steel-tyred, resilient road wheels of the Conqueror heavy gun tank.

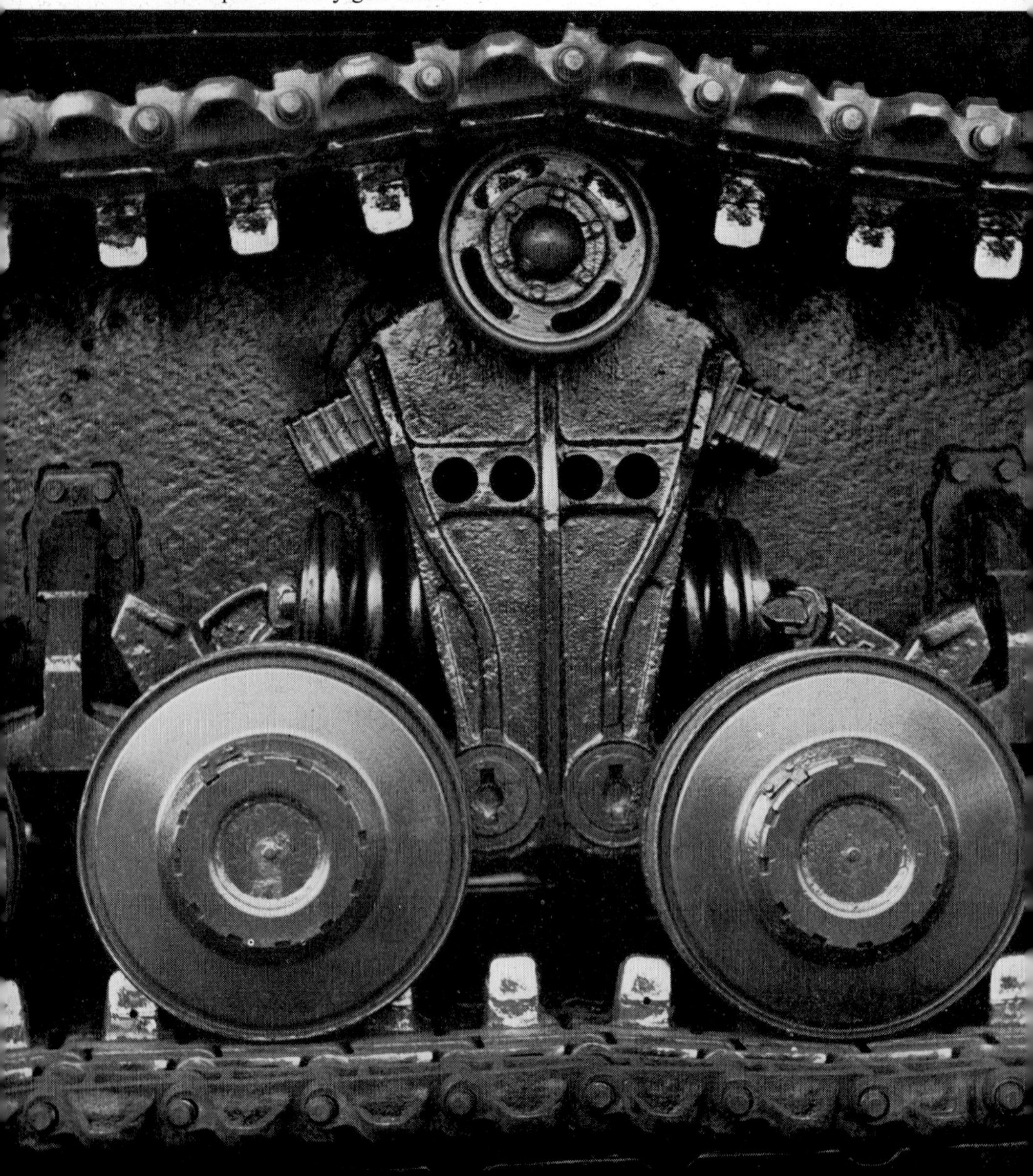

100 – Epoxy resin bonded glass fibre road wheel light enough to be lifted by a young boy; in the background a M41 tank with single-pin track.

101 – United States M48 tank with a double-pin, double-block track.

102 – End connectors of a double-pin single-block track.

103 – United States M56 air-portable 90 mm self-propelled anti-tank gun with a band track.

104 – LVTP5 amphibians negotiating surf.
105 – LVTH6 amphibian of the U.S. Marine Corps followed by LVTP5 carriers.

106 – Covers over the outlets from the water jet propulsion unit of the Russian BTR-50P armoured personnel carrier.

107 – Outlets of the water jet propulsion unit of the Russian PT-76 tank shown open and the right outlet discharging water.

108 – Vickers 37-ton battle tank swimming with the aid of a collapsible flotation screen.

109 – Centurion tank with rigid panel flotation equipment.

110 – German Leopard fording submerged to the turret top.

111 – United States M60A1 tank emerging after the first underwater crossing of the Rhine in 1963.

112 – German Sd.Kfz.251/10 half-track armoured personnel carrier.
113 – United States M3 half-track carrier.

114 – United States M44 Armoured Utility Vehicle, the forerunner of several contemporary armoured personnel carriers.

115 – United States M75 Armoured Infantry Vehicle.

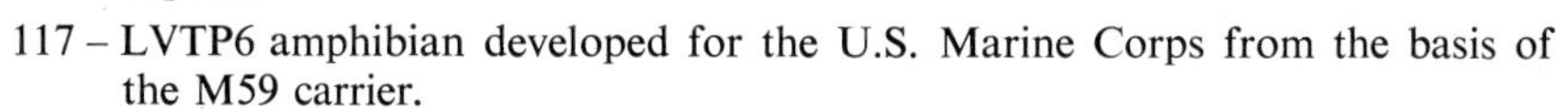
116 – United States M59 Armoured Infantry Vehicle with a ·5 in machine-gun cupola.

117 – LVTP6 amphibian developed for the U.S. Marine Corps from the basis of the M59 carrier.

118 – United States M113 Armoured Personnel Carrier.

119 – M113 carrier propelling itself in water by means of its tracks.

120 – Demonstration of the ease of exit from the M113 carrier due to its rear ramp.
121 – M113 carrier fitted with machine gun shields.

122 – M113 carrier modified into the XM734 with firing ports for fighting from within the carrier.

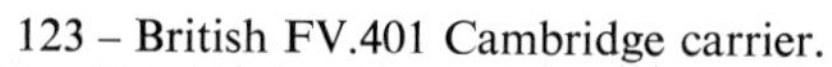

123 – British FV.401 Cambridge carrier.

124 – Prototype of the British FV.432 armoured personnel carrier.

125 – FV.432 armoured personnel carrier with the flotation screen erected and the trim vane hinged forward.

126 – French AMX-VTT carrier with a 7·5 mm machine-gun turret.

127 – Rear view of the AMX-VTT showing the crew facing outwards.

128 – Prototype of the HS.30 carrier with the A.26 Hispano Suiza 20 mm gun turret.
129 – Production version of the German HS.30 carrier.

130 – Austrian Saurer 4K3F carriers.
131 – Side view of the Saurer 4K3F carrier.

132 – Saurer Tartaruga carrier built to a Swiss Army requirement.
133 – Mowag Pirate armoured carrier.

134 – Japanese SU Type 60 carrier.
135 – Henschel HW-K 11 carrier built for Mexico.

136 – Swedish Pbv 301 armoured personnel carrier.

137 – Swedish Pbv 302 armoured personnel carrier.

138 – Pbv 302 carrier swimming offshore.

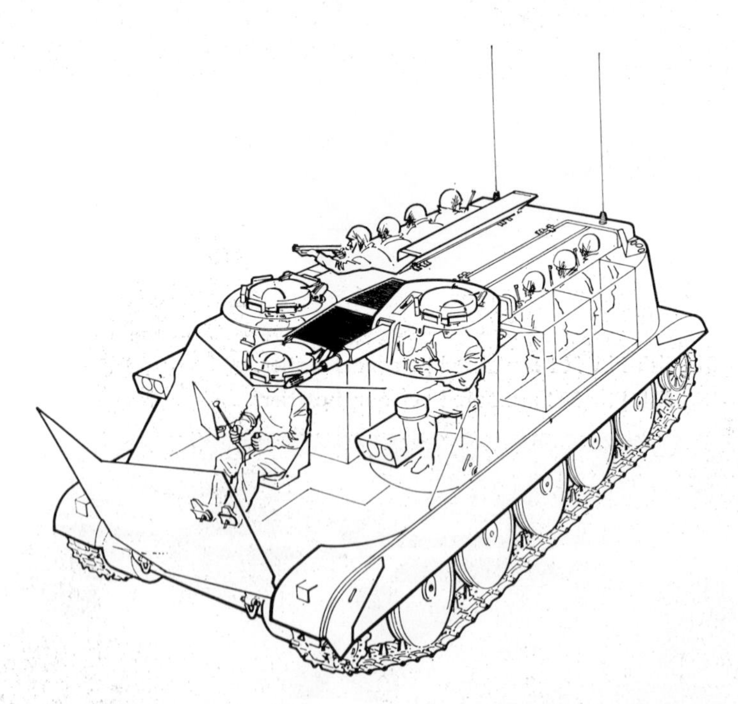

138a – Ghosted view of the Swedish Pbv 302 carrier with the V-shaped trim vane hinged forward.

139 – United States XM 701 Mechanised Infantry Combat Vehicle.
140 – Russian BTR-50P armoured personnel carrier.

141 – Daimler-Benz MTW-1 on trials in 1929.

142 – German Sd.Kfz.234/2 Puma armoured car.

143 – Daimler II Armoured Car.
144 – Ferret Mark 2 scout car.

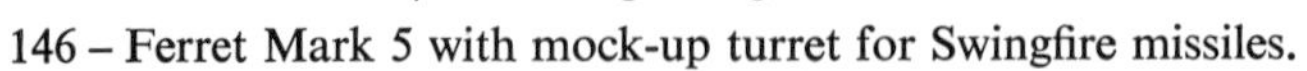
145 – Ferret Mark 2/6 with Vigilant guided missiles.
146 – Ferret Mark 5 with mock-up turret for Swingfire missiles.

147 – Chevrolet-built M38 armoured car.

148 – Prototype of the Alvis Saladin armoured car.

149 – Production version of the Alvis Saladin.

150 – Alvis Saladin with the flotation screen erected.

151 – Alvis Saracen armoured personnel carrier.
152 – FV.1611 armoured truck.

153 – Gendron-Somua armoured car.
154 – Panhard E.B.R. with F.L.11 turret.

155 – Panhard E.B.R. with F.L.10 turret.
156 – Panhard E.B.R. with a 90 mm gun in a F.L.11 turret.

157 – Panhard A.M.L. with H.E.60 turret.
158 – Panhard A.M.L. with a 90 mm gun in a H.90 turret.

159 – Panhard A.M.L. with Entac missiles on a S.A.M.O. 1160 launcher.

160 – F.N. 4RM/62F armoured car with a 90 mm gun.

161 – Russian BTR-152 carrier with a central tyre pressure control system.
162 – Russian BRDM amphibious reconnaissance car with guided missiles.

163 – A rear-engined development of the BRDM reconnaissance car.
164 – Russian BTR-60P amphibious armoured personnel carrier.

165 – Cadillac Gage Commando.

166 – Cadillac Gage Commando propelling itself across a lake by means of its wheels.

167 – Chrysler MAC-1 armoured car built for Mexico.
168 – Chrysler Special Warfare Armoured Transporter.

169 – D.A.F. YP-408 armoured personnel carrier.

170 – Mowag MR 8-01 carrier with four wheel steering.

171 – Mowag amphibious armoured personnel carrier.
172 – Mowag amphibious carrier propelling itself across a lake by means of screws.

173 – Mowag Roland with special bullet proof tyres.

174 – Shorland patrol car.